Maintenance Management Audit
A Step by Step Workbook to Better Your Facility's Bottom Line

Applied Management Engineering, PC, and Harvey H. Kaiser

Maintenance Management Audit

A Step by Step Workbook to Better Your Facility's Bottom Line

Applied Management Engineering, PC, and Harvey H. Kaiser

R.S. MEANS COMPANY, INC.
A Southam Company

CONSTRUCTION CONSULTANTS & PUBLISHERS
100 Construction Plaza
P.O. Box 800
Kingston, MA 02364-0800
(617) 585-7880

The editors for this book were Roger Grant, Mary Greene, and Phillip Waier. Production was supervised by Helen Marcella and Julia Willard. The book and jacket were designed by Norman R. Forgit.

Editor, Reference Books: Mary Greene.

Printed in the United States of America

10 9 8 7 6 5 4 3 2 1

Library of Congress Cataloging in Publication Data

ISBN 0-87629-287-2

Table of Contents

Foreword	vii
Preface	ix
Part I—The Maintenance Management Audit: A Framework	1
Audit Phasing	3
Phase Descriptions	4
Part II—Introduction to the Maintenance Management Audit Process	7
Purpose	9
Effectiveness in Maintenance Management	9
Key Components and Elements of Maintenance Management	11
The Maintenance Management Review Process	13
Part III—Conducting the Maintenance Management Audit	17
Conduct Preliminary Program Review	21
Compile Effectiveness Rating	22
Identify Opportunities for Improvement	27
Establish and Implement an Improvement Action Plan	27
Evaluate Results	28
Part IV—Audit Forms	33
Guideline Checklists	37
Effectiveness Rating Worksheets	74
Effectiveness Rating Summary	84
Part V—Case Study	85

Foreword

Management audits provide a framework for organizations to systematically review, analyze, and recommend improvements in performance. The results of a management audit are a work plan that specifies the areas that need improvement, the appropriate corrective actions, and procedures for monitoring the outcome of these corrective actions. The functions to be reviewed include the more difficult areas of service that require standards of measurement different than those of traditional manufacturing operations. Using a logical format that systematically structures the process enables senior management to select and analyze a variety of different functional areas for analysis and improvement.

The management audit described in this workbook is a review activity designed to assist an organization both in appraising the effectiveness of its facilities operations and improving them in a systematic manner. The audit should be applied as a constructive process, one that encourages managers to engage in self evaluations of their organizations as the review is conducted. The audit system is presented in a workbook format that can be used directly by internal staff, consultants, or a combination of both.

An important role is played by senior management in authorizing the audit process and assuring that its purposes are to improve operational efficiencies and service performance. A steering committee can be appointed by senior management to select the departments to be audited. In this way, managers are less likely to misconstrue the audit as a personnel evaluation. The steering committee should select a broad representation of an organization's functional activities for the audit. The specific aim of a management audit is to provide those responsible for management with an independent, objective, and constructive evaluation of the facility's maintenance management efforts.

Part I provides a generic framework for a maintenance management audit. It identifies the basic phases of a comprehensive audit and describes the specific actions required for each phase. Part II presents an overview of the management audit process: its purpose, effectiveness, key elements, and a general description. Part III describes the specific techniques of the audit and review in some detail, and explains how to use the audit forms to achieve a positive result. The goal is to first identify the key elements of maintenance management. Next, evaluate the status of those elements, and then recommend a plan to achieve overall improvement. Part IV consists of the actual review and audit forms, which can be photocopied and reused each year to perform the Maintenance Management Audit program. Part V of the book is a case study using the Maintenance Management Audit. This example is provided to illustrate the principles, procedures, and methods of the audit system. The case study is based on an institution with conditions in its facilities maintenance organization commonly found by the authors in conducting evaluations of multiple facilities.

The audit system is designed to identify the tasks of a facilities organization seeking to improve effectiveness and efficiency. The growth of these organizations in size, variety of services, and extent of operations has made it increasingly important to audit management methods and performance on a regular basis.

The process outlined in this book can serve in two capacities. First, it provides a documented, step-by-step method of conducting a large scale audit of a facilities maintenance organization. Second, the process can be started at Part III, and used as the preliminary phase of a detailed audit, providing direction by identifying areas that merit the most intensive investigation. Either way, the audit process defines checkpoints of facilities maintenance management and quantifies their effectiveness, setting up a base line for future comparisons.

Preface

Improving productivity in maintenance management is becoming an important challenge to facilities managers. Although this might be considered a routine goal, changing financial conditions and demands to restrain expenditures are forcing facilities managers to examine maintenance management even more closely for opportunities to increase productivity.

Typical operations and maintenance activities can account for 5-15% of the total expenditures of an institution. Management has the responsibility to ensure that the resources made available for maintenance management functions are being employed in the most effective manner possible. A thorough audit of maintenance management functions can provide opportunities for improved program effectiveness, including:

1. Increased levels of service and quality of performance
2. Guidelines for organizational restructuring
3. Introduction of management information systems to assist in meeting productivity and effectiveness goals
4. Better use of resources due to program improvements

This workbook provides techniques for reviewing the key elements in a maintenance management program to improve overall effectiveness. Two stages of a maintenance management program audit are presented. The first involves assembling and evaluating background material in a Preliminary Program Review. With this preparation phase completed, the second stage is to develop an Effectiveness Rating to determine a maintenance organization's relative overall effectiveness. This rating can also correlate with the actual productivity level of the organization and provides a benchmark that can be compared to generally accepted productivity targets. The Effectiveness Rating process also lets management know where to focus its efforts for the most significant improvements. Future evaluations can then measure the effectiveness of any changes in management practices, as compared to the status shown in this baseline survey.

In the development of this workbook, Applied Management Engineering, P.C. and Harvey H. Kaiser, Ph.D. have utilized their extensive experience training personnel and developing and analyzing facilities management programs for private corporations, federal, state, and local governments, and institutes of higher education. The methods presented have evolved from applications that have achieved significant improvements for hundreds of clients, spanning over 30 years of consulting services.

In some facilities management programs, specific opportunities were found to be readily available for immediate improvements. In others, major deficiencies were identified, which led to organizational restructuring and the introduction of more efficient procedures.

The format and techniques of this audit system are most applicable to organizations of a size and complexity that require a work control center for the management of maintenance work. This can range from the smaller size organization with approximately 20-25 skilled tradespeople at a single location, to the largest size maintenance organizations providing services to multiple locations.

We hope that you will find this workbook comprehensive and easy to use. It has been designed so that the procedures can be used by management without extensive training and in a comparatively short period of time. It is understood that circumstances and conditions will vary between organizations that undertake an audit of maintenance management. In the event specific elements are not applicable, there should be no hesitation to modify the materials presented to better address the needs of a unique organization. However, we suggest that, initially, the format outlined in this book should be followed. Then, as future iterations of the audit process take place, modifications can be based on an informed and experienced position.

Acknowledgments

The publication of this book was made possible by all of the officers and staff of Applied Management Engineering, PC. Their efforts and ideas have shaped AME into a firm of unique engineering expertise.

Officers

Robert G. Brooks, Jr., P.E. President
Robert K. Graham, P.E. Vice President, Operations
Douglas W. Kincaid, P.E.Vice President, Business Development

Other Contributing Staff Members

Robert B. Vaughn, Sr. Project Director
Natalie A. Elkino, Sr. Systems Manager
Anna M. Rhoades, Administrative Manager
Cynthia M. Lucero, Administrative Staff

This book would not have been possible without the efforts of William L. Thomas, Special Assistant to AME in Faculty Management. Bill's 40 years of experience provided the framework on which the concepts and procedures in this book were developed. After a successful career with the Naval Facilities Engineering Command, Bill joined AME in 1980 to help enhance our approach to facilities management. His contribution to AME cannot be overstated. For most of his career, Bill had the same request from all his clients: Tell me how well I am running my organization, and what I can do to make it run better? Bill's ability to organize the information needed to answer these questions is essentially the product of this book.

Lastly, the authors would like to gratefully acknowledge the staff at R.S. Means. Ferol Breymann, Acquisitions Editor had the initial confidence in our manuscript to recommend its publication. Mary Greene coordinated the difficult tasks of compiling the authors' notes into a finished product. Roger Grant and Phillip Waier provided important technical reviews to ensure the book would meet current engineering standards.

About the Authors

Applied Management Engineering is a nationally recognized engineering firm helping clients find ways to more effective overall operations. AME has applied proven concepts in facilities management, together with the core disciplines of engineering, to meet the needs of Department of Defense agencies, established colleges and universities, and major U.S. cities. Regular clients include the University of California, the City of San Diego, the State of Virginia, the University of Virginia, the Naval Facilities Engineering Command, and Ferm National Accelerator Laboratory.

In addition to providing a full range of traditional engineering services, AME has prepared several publications on facilities management for the Departments of the Navy and Air Force. These publications serve as policy directives for effective decision-making for improved overall operations.

Harvey H. Kaiser, R.A., Ph.D., is Senior Vice President in charge of Facilities, and Associate Professor of Urban and Regional Planning at Syracuse University. Dr. Kaiser's responsibilities at the university include community relations and the management of general administrative services at the schools' campuses in Syracuse, the Adirondacks, New York City, and Europe.

Dr. Kaiser has lectured extensively at major universities and organizations including the Association of Physical Plant Administrators, the American Institute of Architects, the National Endowment for the Arts, the National Trust for Historic Preservation, the National Association of College and University Business Officers, the New York State Preservation League, and many others. Dr. Kaiser is the author of *The Facilities Manager's Reference* (R.S. Means, 1989) as well as several other books, articles, and monographs.

Part One

The Maintenance Management Audit: A Framework

Part One

The Maintenance Management Audit: A Framework

Audit Phasing

The purpose of a maintenance management audit is to ensure that management is carrying out its mission, meeting its goals and objectives, following proper procedures, and managing resources effectively and efficiently. A framework for the audit process is shown in Figure I.1.

Preliminary suggestions for conducting a management audit are:

- The audit should assess the right things. It must appraise performance in light of sound management principles. Objectives and scope must be clearly defined to ensure a constructive appraisal of an operation's effectiveness.
- The audit should include the participation of the department being reviewed.
- The audit should be objective and constructive. Every effort should be made to ensure that all review participants maintain independent, constructive perspectives.

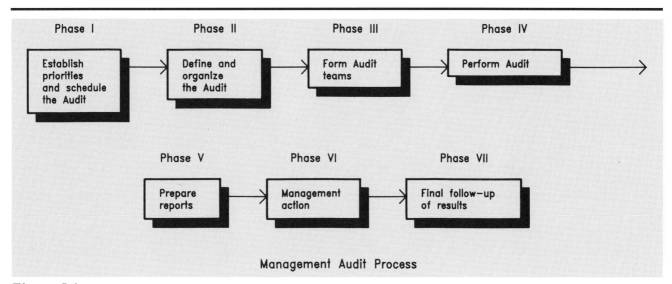

Figure I.1

• The evaluation should be understandable and acceptable. Any management technique or program that people do not understand and accept is likely to be ineffective.

Phase Descriptions

The basic phases, steps, and functional assignments in the management audit process are described below. There can be many variations on the central framework, depending on the organization's size, management style, and organizational structure. Formal, coordinated steps might be necessary for larger organization.

Phase I—Establish Priorities and Schedule Audit

1. Prepare a draft review schedule and nominate activities to be reviewed; suggest priorities and review time frames.
2. Set priorities among areas to be reviewed; issue schedule.
3. Senior managers of the organization should develop a steering committee and determine priorities for departmental reviews. Priorities determine whether or not to review all functional components or to target selected components. A review of the effectiveness and efficiency of the targeted componenets can ultimately result in cost benefits or improved service by applying the management audit process.

Phase II—Define and Organize the Audit

1. Review functional areas and procedures pertinent to the functional area; identify potential audit team members.
2. Establish coordination with department manager(s); discuss the purpose of the audit and potential audit team members—the participants and the timing.
3. Prepare and send questionnaires to department manager(s).
4. Assemble data about the audit area.
5. Prepare preliminary statement of the scope of the audit:
   — Identify the limits of the audit.
   — Prepare a statement of the objectives.
6. Establish a work plan for the audit:
   — Review possible methods of analysis and data collection.
   — Identify criteria to be used in evaluating unit performance.
   — Determine necessary coordinating procedures.
   — Identify audit tasks.
   — Estimate resources needed to conduct the audit.
   — Estimate time requirements to perform the audit.

A high grade performance by the evaluation coordinator and staff in the second phase enables the audit team to carry out its assignment economically, efficiently, and effectively. Three things must happen. First, the coordinator discusses the proposed audit with the manager of the selected department. Next, the staff begins assembling pertinent information which will be turned over to the audit team. Finally, a definition of the audit parameters and an indication of the processes to be examined are proposed in a statement of the scope of the audit.

Phase III—Form the Audit Team

1. Select members for the audit team and arrange with department heads for members' participation.
2. Familiarize the audit team with functional areas and style of work.
3. Confirm and adopt statement of scope of audit.
4. Confirm work plan with department manager(s).
5. Discuss methods and procedures with the audit team.
6. Prepare detailed task plans using functional area outline and orientation material previously assembled by staff.

7. Assign specific tasks to team members.

The coordinator should take the lead in selecting the audit team members, and securing from their respective department directors a temporary release from standing commitments. Candidates for the audit team should be selected from senior supervisory staff representing a cross-section of work planning, skilled trades, material control, and finance/budget management. A key task before any further action is the adoption of a written statement of the scope of the audit. This leads to the team's work plan, time schedule, and assignments of tasks to individual members. The importance of a scope statement cannot be overemphasized.

Phase IV—Perform the Audit

1. Collect data: Review policies and procedures, conduct interviews with unit staff, utilize opinion poll questionnaires, review budget documents. The Guideline Checklists in Part IV identify the types of data to be collected.
2. Organize and analyze. This includes tabulating survey information, summarizing, and organizing interview data, and then interpreting the data.
3. Identify organizational, process, and service problems.

The audit team carries out its active work of analyzing the problems that are uncovered using the information collected. This involves personal observations and interviews, both in and around the unit being audited. In team meetings, impressions should be clarified until the team is ready to make recommendations.

Phase V—Prepare the Report

1. Formulate recommendations of alternative approaches to operations and organizations to assist management in solving identified problems.
2. Determine report format and content.
3. Assign drafting responsibilities; prepare draft of report.
4. Discuss, evaluate, and revise the draft report.
5. Discuss the revised draft report with department manager(s).
6. Prepare a final report and present it to the steering committee.
7. Review, approve, and distribute the final report.

Whether or not the report produces tangible results depends largely on how well Phases V and VI are handled. The audit team's central task is to prepare a report for senior management on the audited unit's degree of success in meeting its objectives and on the unit's major strengths and weaknesses. The report also makes recommendations for management action.

Phase VI—Management Action

1. Submit a plan of action responding to audit team recommendations.
2. Assess audit team report and action plan from department manager(s); discuss with department manager(s) and supervisor, if necessary.
3. Evaluate and approve recommendations to be carried out by department manager(s).
4. Obtain agreement and support from department manager(s) and supervisor on action plan items.

In Phase VI, the organization's determination to effectively manage its resources is tested and demonstrated. The department manager responds to the audit team's final report by proposing a plan of action. After assessing the potential effectiveness of the plan (in meeting the report's findings and recommendations), agreement must be obtained on a systematic course of action. The department manager and the supervisor are expected to initiate the necessary changes indicated in the report.

Phase VII—Final Follow-up of Results

1. Monitor the implementation process.
2. Submit a progress report on implementation to the steering committee.
3. Critique review activity and results (include evaluation of project methodology, suggestions for changes in procedures, etc.).
4. Submit closing report to steering committee and chief executive officer.

During Phase VII, the evaluation's effectiveness as a long-range tool comes into focus. Achieving the goals included in the department manager's plan may take anywhere from several months to more than a year. Desired outcomes may not be perceptible until a similar amount of time has elapsed. The review cycle comes to a close with a brief, final report on the audit and a summary of the results achieved.

Part Two

Introduction to the Maintenance Management Audit Process

Part Two

Introduction to the Maintenance Management Audit Process

Purpose

An audit of a specific functional service area, such as maintenance management, focuses on efficiency of operations. In contrast to the more traditional measurement of manufacturing productivity, where units of labor and material can be compared to costs and rates of production, factors must be identified that can lead to improvements in both cost efficiencies and levels and quality of service.

The format of this workbook is designed to answer the critical question: How well are we protecting our investment in facilities? The maintenance management audit and review process answers that question by providing an appraisal of the organization's maintenance management system. The results offer management the opportunity to seek improvements for increased efficiency and more effective utilization of available resources. The audit is designed to meet the needs of all organizations that have a maintenance component by utilizing common factors to evaluate performance.

The first step is a systematic review and evaluation of existing procedures, practices, and supporting documents through the Preliminary Program Review. This process familiarizes the person or persons conducting the audit and review with the maintenance management organization and operation in preparation for compiling the Effectiveness Rating. It also provides early insights into possible problem areas.

The second step in the audit, the Effectiveness Rating, provides a measure for comparing the organization's maintenance management productivity to accepted standards. With this stage of the audit completed, recommendations for a formal improvement Action Plan can be developed, including specific actions, goals, and timetables.

The process can be repeated periodically and comparisons made against the base line of the initial study to measure the effectiveness of improvement actions taken.

Effectiveness in Maintenance Management

To assess a maintenance management program, one should look at four factors that provide an overall indication of program effectiveness.

1. **Productivity**—the portion of a worker's time that is directly productive.
2. **Performance**—how well the individual is working, i.e., is work being completed as planned?

3. **Work Quality**—are they producing a satisfactory work product.
4. **Priority**—effective allocation of available time to the most important tasks.

Productivity is how a worker's time is spent.

- Productivity is defined as the percentage of total hours spent on *directly productive* activities. It can be measured with considerable accuracy by the statistical technique of work sampling, which is very time consuming.
- Results of a number of studies conducted at various facility maintenance shops indicated that productivity at most shops ranged between 38% and 48%, with an overall average of 43%. Extensive studies for the Department of Defense and several higher education institutions confirm these ranges and average levels of productivity.
- Optimum productivity is usually considered to range between 65% and 70%. However, a more reasonable initial target would be 55-60%.
- With a target productivity of 55% and the average actual productivity of 43%, the potential gain represents over a one-fourth improvement (12/43 = 28%). This is very conservative and attainable. Achieving an optimum productivity of 70% would result in an almost two-thirds gain in productivity (27/43 = 63%).

Using these figures, potential gains in productivity can range from 12% to 63%.

Performance is how efficiently a worker's time is spent.

- Performance is defined as the percentage of *actual hours* used to perform a task, as compared with the *planned hours* established for accomplishing the work.
- The accuracy of the measure of performance depends on the validity of the planned hours.
- If the planned hours are established on the basis of past performances, inefficiencies may be "built-in" and not identified.
- Estimates by qualified estimators can provide a useful base for performance measurement if carefully applied. Although in-house staff may be available to perform this task, it is preferable to retain consultants for more objective analyses.
- Ideally, planned hours will be based on the application of engineered performance standards.
- Potential performance improvements can easily range from 10% to 25%.

Quality is the factor that identifies *how well* the work was performed. Measurement of quality is more subjective and is usually not quantified. The amount of rework, number of customer complaints, and general customer perceptions from surveys are some direct indications of the quality of completed work.

Priority assures that the most important work within the overall maintenance and repair workload is being accomplished. This involves three principal features:

- All existing maintenance and repair deficiencies must be identified to ensure all work requirements are considered. A comprehensive periodic condition inspection is the only way this can be accomplished with certainty.
- A meaningful priority criteria must be established and applied consistently to all work items.
- Reports of work accomplished by priority must be routinely provided to management for evaluation.

As a general rule, the better the maintenance management system is designed and utilized, the more these four factors will be enhanced, resulting in a more effective overall maintenance operation.

Key Components and Elements of Maintenance Management

The four factors indicating efficiency and effectiveness—*productivity, performance, work quality, and priority*—overlap in many areas of the maintenance organization. An analysis of how maintenance is managed and performed uses five basic components to evaluate the effectiveness of a maintenance management program. These components are further subdivided into *key elements*.

Use of these five basic components and key elements has been developed and tested in a variety of audit studies for different types of profit and nonprofit organizations, including private corporations, local governments, federal government agencies, and institutes of higher education. Alternative arrangements and factors can be developed for special applications. For example, a maintenance management organization may share some functions with other departments, such as purchasing, inventory control, or management information systems. Some organizations may operate under organizational structures that consolidate portions of workload identification and work planning into a single function. The workbook user should become familiar with the structure of the basic components and key elements and determine whether they are appropriate for use as presented or need to be adapted for their own unique conditions. However, as stated in the Preface, variations on the forms, processes and procedures should only be undertaken after becoming familiar with the audit process, after several iterations.

The five basic components and key elements are listed in Figure II.1

A review of Figure II.1 may raise questions about terms and definitions that are answered in the following sections of Part II. Basically, the Maintenance Management Audit has been structured to follow the actual maintenance management process, but is set up such that components and/or elements can be regrouped, added to, or deleted to match your particular type of maintenance management organization. The five basic components follow the sequential steps of the major functional areas of maintenance management illustrated in Figure II.2.

The first basic component, **Organization** (Figure II.1), includes the essential management activities that guide policies and procedures. This component is broken down into six elements. For this component, the organizational structure is evaluated to identify lines of responsibility and position descriptions. The formal use of manuals or other guides to define who plans and supervises and what they do is also covered in this section.

The next component, **Workload Identification**, addresses the way(s) in which needed work is brought to the attention of the maintenance organization and documented. The maintenance department should have a formal procedure for recording work generated by various sources.

Under **Work Planning**, the methods used to perform work are evaluated. Prioritizing, planning, estimating, and budgeting are all tasks that control the flow of work accomplished by shop forces and contractors. Part of work planning is juggling and merging the available funds with the priority work items to ensure that work is performed in a timely and cost effective fashion.

The **Work Accomplishment** component describes various support activities that enable the maintenance management organization to perform

Basic Components and Key Elements of the Maintenance Management Audit

A. Organization
    1. Organization structure
    2. Policies, Rules, Services
    3. Work Control (functions)
    4. Work Control Center (staffing)
    5. Shop Organization
    6. Shop Supervision & Planning (functions)

B. Workload Identification
    1. Facilities Inventory
    2. Facility Condition Inspection
    3. Work Request Procedure
    4. Equipment Inventory
    5. Preventive Maintenance (equipment)
    6. Service Work
    7. Routine, Recurring Work
    8. Work Requirements Documentation

C. Work Planning
    1. Priority Criteria
    2. Work Classification
    3. Alterations & Improvement (A/I) Work—Approval
    4. Work Order (WO) Preparation
    5. Backlog Requirements for M & R
    6. Backlog Deferred Maintenance & Repair
    7. Budget Execution Plan
    8. Backlog of Funded Work

D. Work Accomplishment
    1. Shop Scheduling & Planning Procedures
    2. Craft and Material Availability
    3. Training Program
    4. Shop Spaces, Tools, Equipment
    5. Storeroom Operation
    6. Transportation
    7. Supervisory Practices
    8. Use of Contracts

E. Appraisal
    1. Management Information System (MIS)
    2. Performance Measurement
    3. productivity Measurement
    4. Variance Reviews
    5. Facility History Records
    6. Equipment History Records
    7. Trend Data

Figure II.1

efficiently. Executing work assignments properly requires readily available personnel, materials, equipment, and transportation. Staff requires training and supervision, and contracting procedures should be well defined.

The **Appraisal** component summarizes the information system features needed to monitor the comparison of actual to planned results. Management should have available adequate information to evaluate both the differences between budgeted and actual costs, and performance. Reports documenting completed work provide management with a basis for control and direction for corrective actions.

The Maintenance Management Review Process

The review process outlined in this workbook is designed to evaluate the effectiveness of the existing maintenance management program. By assessing each of the key elements, one can obtain an overview of program effectiveness. This overview provides:

• A program effectiveness rating
• Identification of areas for potential improvement
• A broad indication of potential productivity gains

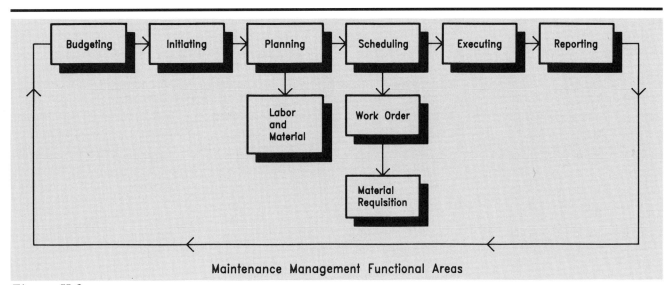

Figure II.2

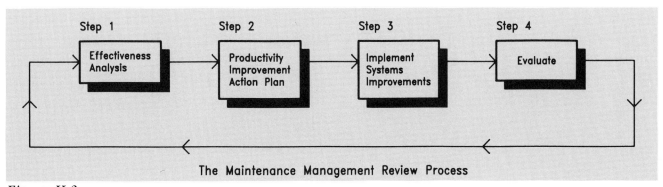

Figure II.3

The overall review process, together with a complete action program, is illustrated in Figure II.3. Note that some or all of the review process may require the assistance of consultants, depending on the size of the facility, the schedule, and the resources available for completing the process. Consultants may be preferred in cases where objectivity is a concern of senior management or where staff is unavailable to complete part or all of the audit process.

If an outside consultant is to be used, the facility managers should seek a firm of primarily an industrial engineering background. A design-oriented engineering firm is clearly not appropriate for this type of study. In any event, the facility manager should require several recent references of similar studies. The manager should obtain direct feedback about the personnel, the quality of the work, and the client's overall satisfaction with the firm.

The first step of the maintenance management review process is the maintenance management effectiveness analysis, which is designed to improve productivity. This analysis is a procedure to develop the following understanding of the maintenance organization:

- How is it organized?
- How does it function?
- How effective is its operation?

The effectiveness analysis procedure includes a numerical rating system to identify and measure each of the key elements. The subtotal of these key elements and the total of the Effectiveness Rating provide a subjective quantification of overall program effectiveness.

A maintenance management program that has all components fully implemented will achieve an **excellent** rating. Experience has shown that there is a close correlation between overall program effectiveness and direct productivity as illustrated in Figure II.4. Higher system effectiveness means higher productivity.

Industry sources (the Department of Defense, college and university publications) put maximum productivity of a facilities maintenance organization at 65%. It follows that maximum program effectiveness would be 100% (if maximum productivity obtainable is indeed 65%).

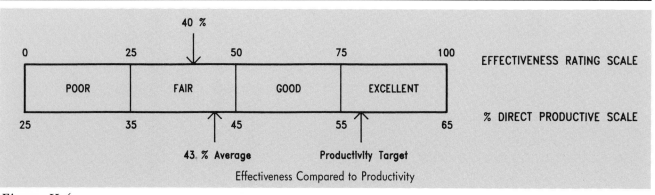

Figure II.4

14

Conversely, even a poorly run program (i.e., one that is 0% effective) produces productivity figures at a minimum of 25%.

The authors (Applied Management Engineering), in producing the Maintenance Management Audit, took 25% increments of the Effectiveness scale and assigned break points for the ratings of *poor, fair, good,* and *excellent.*

A review of productivity studies completed (by AME and others) showed that a typical or average facility organization had productivity ratings of 38% to 48% (with an overall average of 43%). This range defined typical conditions. Above the range of 48% to 55% was set at *excellent.*

On the lower end of the spectrum, most poorly run organizations have studies that record 30% to 40% as the most frequently recurring range observed. Therefore, 35% was set as the break point for *poor* and *fair.*

Part Three

Conducting the Maintenance Management Audit

Part Three
Conducting the Maintenance Management Audit

This workbook is designed for use by in-house personnel familiar with their maintenance organization. However, our experience in conducting audits confirms that objectivity can be difficult to achieve. Team involvement in the audit should be considered as a way to obtain a more balanced perspective, particularly in determining how much emphasis implementation should be given in each of the various key elements. Use of consultants may also be considered to ensure objectivity and accuracy of the audits. However, if consultants are used, they should be thoroughly familiar with maintenance operations of a similar organization, rather than just having general organizational or fiscal management experience.

The first step in an audit of this kind, performed either in-house or by consultants, is to obtain a clear understanding of the audit's goals. This workbook sets the goal of providing a link between an assessment of the maintenance organization's effectiveness and recommendations for achieving improvements. Reasons for conducting the audit may differ. Senior management may request a general evaluation of how efficiently resources are currently being used; they may be concerned about cost containment or improving organization relationships. Maintenance management may want a detailed review of the status and utilization of maintenance program system elements, e.g., work control, material control, or use of contract services. In any of these cases, the results can identify potential improvements.

A specific person should be designated responsible for overseeing the audit. Where several staff members will be involved in the study, their specific assignments should be delegated and discussed to ensure understanding of their respective roles in the audit.

The documentation used to produce the effectiveness analysis is illustrated in Figure III.1, and includes the following:

- **Five Effectiveness Rating Worksheets** (one for each basic component), which contain rating criteria for each related key element.
- **Guideline Checklists** which provide more detailed indicators of appropriate actions related to each key element.
- **One Effectiveness Rating Summary Sheet** which is issued to rate each element and component, and to compile the overall rating.

A complete set of forms used for the Effectiveness Analysis and Rating Summary (Figure III.1) is included in Part IV of this workbook.

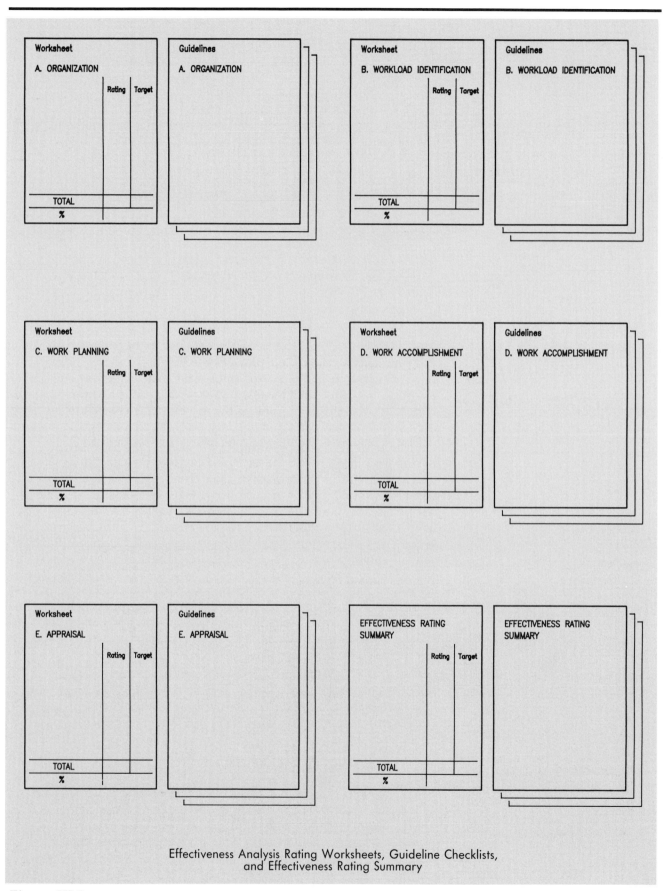

Effectiveness Analysis Rating Worksheets, Guideline Checklists,
and Effectiveness Rating Summary

Figure III.1

The use of the Guideline Checklists and Effectiveness Rating worksheets, first for a review of the maintenance program, and second to develop an Effectiveness Rating, provides a framework for a thorough evaluation of important aspects of how maintenance is *managed, performed,* and *evaluated.* Users should understand the purpose of the Effectiveness Analysis, and then thoroughly scan the forms to familiarize themselves with the process. Terms and criteria should be reviewed and modifications considered to better fit the organization being evaluated. Changes should be made, however, only after a thorough initial review is completed. It is also a good idea to document the estimate for all changes in detail for future reference.

A complete audit consists of the following actions:
- Conduct Preliminary Program Review (using Guideline Checklists).
- Compile Effectiveness Rating (using Effectiveness Rating Worksheets).
- Identify opportunities for improvement (using Effectiveness Rating Summary Sheet).
- Establish and implement an Improvement Action Plan (by reviewing the answers to the Guideline Checklist questions).
- Evaluate results.

Conduct Preliminary Program Review

The first step of the Maintenance Management Audit is the Preliminary Program Review. The review provides the foundation for the audit by developing the basic information upon which all subsequent decisions are made. It makes use of the Guideline Checklists (Part IV) which contain individual worksheets for each of the key elements covered in the audit.

The reader should refer to the Guideline Checklist in Part IV for A-1, Organization (Structure) following Figure IV.1 for the form and content of a typical checklist. In answering the questions on the checklist, the reviewer should address two basic issues: the degree of implementation and how well the item is being accomplished. A checklist item that is not being implemented or is implemented poorly will stand out as an item for the Action Program.

Completing the checklists should be done with a thorough understanding of the Maintenance Management Audit's process and its purposes. The answers should be noted on the checklists and could be expressed as "yes," "complete," "partial," "no," or "not applicable." It is essential that more detailed notes be taken on the current status of each key element and of actions, additional studies, or decisions that might be considered to improve effectiveness.

Note that the Guideline Checklists are generally organized to follow the Effectiveness Rating Worksheet under the same title. It will be helpful to refer to the Effectiveness Rating Worksheet when answering the Guideline Checklist questions to complete the process more efficiently. The Worksheets use a rating point system of 1 for a "yes" answer, or a 0 for a "no" answer to a Guideline question.

The Effectiveness Rating Worksheets convert each response to questions on the Guideline Checklists into a summary statement based on those questions. For instance, on Checklist A-1 Organization (Structure), the first question is, "Is an organization chart readily available which reflects the current structure and accurately identifies all components, positions, and interrelationships?"

The corresponding Effectiveness Rating Worksheet for item A.1 lists two statements. They are, "Documentation not prepared or outdated," and "Organization chart."

A "yes" answer to the question would indicate to the reviewer to assign (or circle) a value of "1."

In other cases there may be several Guideline questions that can only be answered as a partial "yes." In these instances, the reviewer must decide which rating to apply, based on his or her best judgment of the overall effectiveness of the element being rated and the degree to which future actions may be required to achieve full effectiveness. For example, in rating A-1, Organization (Structure), the reviewer may have determined that the answer to the first question was "yes," answers to the next three questions were a partial "yes," and answers to the remaining questions were "no." In this instance, the judgment was made to give a rating of 3.

In answering the questions, the reviewer should be careful to avoid quick assumptions. For example, if a procedure is established, but it is currently ineffective, it should not be considered complete. The degree of effectiveness and the nature of the problems should be identified, along with potential actions or further studies required and an indication of benefits that may result.

After all the checklist questions have been studied and answered, the reviewer will have considered and accumulated information on the status of 220 specific items that contribute to the overall effectiveness of the maintenance management program. The next step is to summarize and assess this information.

Compile Effectiveness Rating

The Effectiveness Rating introduces a structured approach for summarizing review findings and provides for quantifying and evaluating overall effectiveness. The Effectiveness Rating process makes use of the five Effectiveness Rating Worksheets (Part IV, Section B) and the Effectiveness Rating Summary (Part IV, Section C).

There are Effectiveness Rating Worksheets for each of the five major components of the Maintenance Management Audit. The first, the worksheet for rating the organization (A. Organization), consists of six major elements with an assigned weighting factor for each element and a maximum target rating of 168 points as shown in the Target column.

Figure III.2 shows a sample section of the Effectiveness Rating Worksheet for the major component "A. Organization." The legend across the top of the Worksheet has four columns:

1. The number of the major element (which corresponds to a Guideline Checklist);
2. The title of the major element and under it the listing of items to be rated;
3. A rating column divided into a column on the left with an entry of 0 or 1 to be circled for a "yes" answer or left uncircled for a "no" answer (the reviewer may prefer to enter a notation of a fraction for a "partial" answer), and a column on the right with the value of a weighting factor multiplied by the total of the circled choices; and
4. A column with a Target rating for the major component.

Weighting factors delineate the relative importance attributed to various elements. The factors have been established through the authors' experience in developing maintenance management audits for a variety of organizations and locations. These factors can be modified to fit the special characteristics and experience of an organization in applying the audit, but modifications should only be done when the user has become familiar with the audit process. The target rating number results from multiplying the suggested weighting factor by a maximum of 4, the total for each section if all questions in the Guideline Checklists were answered "yes."

In the completed example in Figure III.2, the observed rating is 21, compared with the target of 28. The sample has been completed by the following steps:

Step 1. A possible choice of a "yes" or "no" is circled or left uncircled in the left hand column under "Rating," as determined by reference to the Guideline Checklist and additional information collected during the Preliminary Program Review. In the example, three entries have been circled as "yes" answers.

Step 2. The total of the circled choices (3) is entered in the blank space next to the weighting factor in the left hand column under "Rating."

Step 3. The weighting factor (7) is multiplied by the selected choice (3) and an entry of 21 is placed in the right hand column under "Rating."

The total observed rating of all elements on a worksheet for a given component can be compared with the total target rating for that component. Figure III.3 is an example of a completed Worksheet for the "A. Organization" component. It shows a total observed point rating of 92, as compared with the target of 168. The percentage of the actual rating versus the target rating can also be computed and recorded (as shown in Figure III.3) as 55%.

The totals of all the recorded ratings on the Effectiveness Rating Worksheets are later entered on the Effectiveness Rating Summary, and the recorded rating percentage of the maximum target points is calculated by dividing the observed rating by the target rating. The result is an overall Effectiveness Rating for the maintenance management program. Figure III.4 is an example of a completed Effectiveness Rating Summary sheet. It shows an overall rating of 384 points, as compared with the overall target of 960 points, which is 40%. This falls within the 25% to 50% range, which indicates an overall rating of "fair" as shown in the scale in Figure I.4.

B. Effectiveness Rating Worksheet

A. Organization			RATING	TARGET
1.	**Organization (Structure)**	7 x **3**	*21*	28
	Documentation not prepared or outdated	0		
	Organization Chart	①		
	Functional Statements	①		
	Job Descriptions	①		
	Active Updating Procedure	1		

Figure III.2

Effectiveness Rating Worksheet

A. Organization

			RATING	TARGET
1.	**Organization (Structure)**	7 x **3**	21	28
	Documentation not prepared or outdated	0		
	Organization Chart	①		
	Functional Statements	①		
	Job Descriptions	①		
	Active Updating Procedure	1		
2.	**Policies, Rules, Services**	7 x **2**	14	28
	Documentation not prepared or outdated	0		
	General policies, rules written	①		
	Complete policies, rules written, distributed	①		
	Complete services, written, distributed	1		
	Active updating procedure	1		
3.	**Work Control (Functions)**	9 x **1**	9	36
	Independent work control function not established	0		
	Independent work control function established	①		
	All basic work control responsibilities assigned	1		
	Process and manage total workload	1		
	Overview evaluation for effectiveness	1		
4.	**Work Control (Staffing)**	8 x **2**	16	32
	Clerical only	0		
	Work Reception, trained	①		
	Planning Staff: adequate, trained	①		
	Inspection Staff: adequate, trained	1		
	Management analysis function	1		
5.	**Shop Organization**	5 x **4**	20	20
	Documentation not prepared or outdated	0		
	Shop functions, policies, rules documented, distributed	①		
	Lines of authority clear, minimum vertical levels	①		
	Related crafts grouped together	①		
	Organization reviewed for effectiveness, past two years	①		

Figure III.3

Effectiveness Rating Worksheet

A. Organization			RATING	TARGET
6.	**Shop Supervision and Planning (Functions)**	6 x **2**	12	24
	Documentation not prepared or outdated	0		
	Supervisory ratios appropriate	①		
	Coordination of multi-craft jobs	①		
	Supervisory Coverage: shifts, others	1		
	Planning functions established	1		
Additional Comments				
		TOTAL POINTS	92	168
		PERCENTAGE	55%	

Figure III.3 (cont.)

Effectiveness Rating Summary

	Action Items	CURRENT RATING	TARGET	
A. Organization		(92)	(168)	
1. Organization (Structure)		21	28	
2. Policies, Rules, Services		14	28	
3. Work Control Center (Functions)		9	36	X
4. Work Control Center (Staffing)		16	32	
5. Shop Organization		20	20	
6. Shop Supervision & Planning (Functions)		12	24	
B. Workload Identification		(60)	(192)	
1. Facilities Inventory	A	5	20	X
2. Facility Condition Inspection	A	0	36	X
3. Work Request Procedure		12	16	
4. Equipment Inventory		5	20	X
5. Preventive Maintenance (Equipment)		18	24	
6. Service Work		0	24	X
7. Routine, Recurring Work		6	24	X
8. Work Requirements Documentation		14	28	
C. Work Planning		(87)	(208)	
1. Priority Criteria		7	28	X
2. Work Classification		7	28	X
3. Alterations & Improvement (A/I) Work — Approval		20	20	
4. Work Order (WO) Preparation		20	40	
5. Budget Requirements for M&R		7	28	X
6. Backlog Deferred Maintenance & Repair	A	6	24	X
7. Budget Execution Plan	A	5	20	X
8. Backlog of Funded Work	A	15	20	
D. Work Accomplishment		(112)	(212)	
1. Shop Scheduling & Planning Procedures		16	32	
2. Craft and Material Availability		12	24	
3. Training Program	A	6	24	X
4. Shop Spaces, Tools, Equipment		28	28	
5. Storeroom Operation		12	24	
6. Transportation		10	20	
7. Supervisory Practices		28	28	
8. Use of Contracts	A	0	32	X
E. Appraisal		(33)	(180)	
1. Management Information System (MIS)	A	8	32	X
2. Performance Measurement		6	24	X
3. Productivity Measurement		0	24	X
4. Variance Reviews		0	24	X
5. Facility History Records		6	24	X
6. Equipment History Records		6	24	X
7. Trend Data		7	28	X
TOTAL POINTS		384	960	
PERCENTAGE RATING		40%		

Figure III.4

26

Identify Opportunities for Improvement

A review of the Effectiveness Rating Summary will very quickly identify those elements with low observed ratings. In the example in Figure III.4, 20 elements have been identified and marked with an "X" as potential areas of improvement. Each of these elements should be examined by reviewing the information compiled during the Preliminary Program Review, and determinations made whether actions or further studies are required in order to achieve improvements. A list of potential actions can then be compiled and evaluated. Considerations regarding each potential action should include:

- Identification of potential benefits
- Amount of effort, time, and cost involved
- Prerequisites required
- Impact on other activities
- Availability of required expertise and support

At this point, decisions should be made concerning which actions should and can be pursued. Inspection of the ratings will indicate where gains can be made, either by immediate attention or through more lengthy detailed studies. Prioritizing actions will require choices. For example, where one key element under a basic component offers a rapid response but low productivity improvements, action may be delayed to obtain significant benefits from comprehensive studies of all items in a key element. In some cases, the most difficult choices will be where changes in personnel assignments are necessary. Reassignment or replacement of staff should be done deliberately to ensure continuity of operations.

Establish and Implement an Improvement Action Plan

After evaluating the review results and identifying improvement actions that are determined appropriate for implementation, an Improvement Action Plan should be developed.

The first step is the assignment of responsibility for leading or coordinating the effort. This should include an initial determination and discussion of the plans, objectives, and desired results; the role of the leader including responsibilities and authority; and an overall indication of parameters such as the item's priority, time requirements, and resources necessary and available to accomplish the desired results.

These general determinations must be made prior to establishing a working plan. For each primary action, this plan should identify all supplementary tasks, timetables with planned start and target completion dates, personnel responsible for specific tasks, and all other resources that will be required. This plan should be formally approved by management and thoroughly discussed with all involved personnel to ensure their understanding and agreement. The active interest, participation, and support of management is essential to achieving the anticipated results.

If the plan indicates an extended period of time and/or involves a number of prerequisite or concurrent activities, it would be helpful to establish and utilize a planning and tracking procedure such as a GANTT (bar) chart or Critical Path (CPM) diagram. Explanations of these scheduling techniques are given in standard industrial engineering texts and in handbooks such as *Means Scheduling Manual*. Having a schedule in place for improvement actions will provide a structured plan for documenting and systematically reporting status information, and for monitoring and controlling progress.

The following is a general example of the process by which an Improvement Action Plan is created. After the 20 areas of potential improvement identified in Figure III.4 were reviewed, eight were selected for action and are marked "A." A detailed action plan for each of these areas should then be developed as discussed above.

An example of an Improvement Action Plan for a key element that received a low rating on Figure III.4 is illustrated by "Facilities Inventory," item B.1 under B. Workload Identification."

The types of decisions that should be considered are suggested by questions in the Guideline Checklist titled "B-1 Facility Inventory" (page 43):

- Assign lead responsibility.
- Determine level of detail to be collected, such as:
  — *General Data*: Facility name and identification number (if used), age, gross square feet, type of construction, current replacement value, users, etc.
  — *Detail Data*: List of facility components and systems with type of material, size, capacity, etc., of each.
  — *Usage Data*: Areas/user spaces, characteristics, adequacy, etc.

- Establish coding and recording procedures.
- Estimate time required to conduct inventory.
- Determine facilities/priorities to be inventoried.
- Identify names of personnel available to participate.
- Commit time to be made available for each participant.
- Establish target completion date and weekly schedules.
- Implement plan and record progress.

Figure III.5 illustrates a basic master planning format which can be used for overall control of an Improvement Action project (This example is based on key elements in Figure III.4 with low ratings). A similar procedure can be used to plan and track each individual action.

Evaluate Results

The evaluation of results of an Improvement Action Plan should be considered as a three-stage effort. In the first stage, the effort is initially concerned with implementation, so evaluation focuses on the status and tasks required to complete the action. This evaluation can be enhanced if an effective reporting procedure is incorporated as an integrated part of the Action Plan to track the progress of implementation against targets.

Maintaining accountability for results of the Action Plan recommendations is extremely important. Supervision and staff must share the conviction that changes and improvements are necessary and that they have the full support of senior management. A steering committee can be an effective monitoring force by requiring periodic reports from line managers and discussing the results. As implementation progresses, steering committee action may be deferred for transition of new managers, or to accommodate reorganization.

In the second stage, evaluation centers around the use and benefits of individual actions as they are incorporated into the routine operation of the organization. Depending on the nature of the action, benefits sometimes may not be immediate or readily observed, and persistent follow-up may be required to ensure that results are fully evaluated.

In this stage of the evaluation, it is also useful to develop an assessment of the audit process and key factors and components used in the audit. The audit process will be of maximum benefit where there is feedback between the line supervision and staff and the steering committee charged with evaluating results.

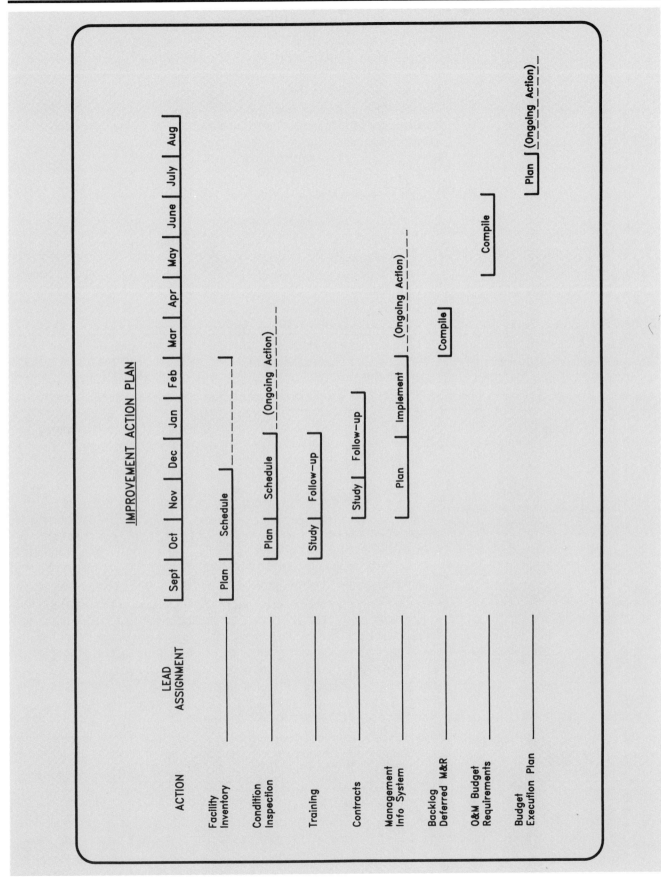

Figure III.5

29

Figure III.6 is a questionnaire for assessing the audit process:

In the final stage, the overall effect of the improvement actions should be evaluated as part of the annual basic review and rating process. This will provide a positive measure for comparison with the original base line and will identify specific areas which have shown improvement or may require further action.

Recommendations from the evaluation process should be incorporated into reviews of the progress achieved on the Action Plan. Reviews should also address the issue of whether productivity gains were achieved, conditions are the same, or have deteriorated.

Results Questionnaire

1. Was the scope and purpose adequately explained and understood by the line staff participating in the audit?

2. Critique the overall audit process. Any recommendations for improvements?

3. How would you rate the effectiveness of the steering committee?

4. Was the Preliminary Program Review adequate in collection of documents, and was it performed with the use of the Guideline Checklists?

5. Should the content of the Guideline Checklists be modified? Items deleted or added?

6. Was the Effectiveness Rating part of the audit understandable and completed consistently and objectively?

7. Should the key factors and major components of the Effectiveness Ratings be modified? Items deleted or added?

8. Recommend any changes in the weighting factors for the major components.

9. Staff time and costs, including consultants, incurred in the audit should be summarized. Was the process completed efficiently and effectively?

10. Was the implementation of the Action Plan performed thoroughly to achieve maximum benefits?

Figure III.6

Part Four

Audit Forms

Part Four

Audit Forms

This part contains a complete set of documents, including:

Part A—Guideline Checklists (Figures IV.1 through IV.37)

Part B—Effectiveness Rating Worksheets (Figures IV.38 through IV.42)

Part C—Effectiveness Rating Summary Sheet (Figure IV.43)

The organization of the Guideline Checklists and Rating Worksheets provides for an initial review in which basic components are targeted because of observed problems. Although the audit process has been organized for a comprehensive review of all elements involved in maintenance management, a selected review of components may be prioritized as appropriate for a specific set of conditions.

The Guideline Checklists address key elements used in the Maintenance Management Audit process. Each checklist includes questions that are converted to a rating for the key elements listed on the Effectiveness Rating Worksheets that follow. The reviewer should review and become familiar with the Effectiveness Rating Worksheets and the Guideline Checklists for all of the basic components before proceeding to answer questions.

You will note that there are five Effectiveness Rating Worksheets, one for each basic component, and there are individual Guideline Checklists for each of the 37 key elements listed on the Worksheets. There may be more than one Guideline Checklist question for a Worksheet entry to assist in making a rating. Headings in bold face on the Guideline Checklists correspond to a rating item on the Effectiveness Rating Worksheets.

The rating criteria is designed to cover the broad scope of effective maintenance management and are generally applicable to a wide range of maintenance organizations. However, there may be exceptional situations where specific criteria may not be considered appropriate. Users are encouraged, once they are familiar and comfortable with the audit system, to change those items to fit their own special conditions. For example, elements can be added or deleted, and weighting factors can be modified to fit the requirements of the organization. In these instances, as long as the target is revised to match the change, the remainder of the process can be completed as described.

A typical key element on an Effectiveness Rating Worksheet begins with a question about whether an item does or does not exist. The items that follow have one or more corresponding questions to help in making a decision on giving a score by circling the rating for a "yes" answer.

For example, look at the first Guideline Checklist titled "A-1 Organization" (Structure) and the Effectiveness Rating Worksheet basic component titled "A. Organization" (Figures IV.1 and IV.38). This particular Checklist provides questions for that key element only. The following five Checklists provide the rest of the questions to complete this "Organization" Rating Worksheet. Note that on the checklist the bold-faced words over the questions correspond to the items for the first key element to be rated, i.e., "1. Organization (Structure)." The next Guideline Checklist titled "A-2. Policies, Rules, Services" provides questions for the next key element on the Effectiveness Rating Worksheet.

The reviewer should compare each question or questions on the checklist to the corresponding item on the appropriate Rating Worksheet and decide whether there is "no," "yes," or partial answer to a question. If the answer is "yes," then the number 1 under the "Rating" column should be circled; if the answer is "no" then the "Rating" should be left uncircled. After the Checklist for a key element has been reviewed and ratings circled or left uncircled, the circled items should be added up and the total entered in the blank space next to the weighting factor. This entry is then multiplied by the weighting factor and the result placed in the right-hand column under "Rating." When all key elements on a Rating Worksheet have been rated, the entries in the right-hand column under "Rating" are added up and entered as the "Total Points" for a basic component.

The process is repeated for the remaining basic components on the Effectiveness Rating Worksheets to complete the review.

The Effectiveness Rating Summary compiles all the key element ratings and their targets. Items on the Summary identified as potential areas for improvement because of a wide disparity between the rating and the target should receive immediate action or further study.

A. Guideline Checklists

A-1 Organization (Structure)

Organization Chart

* Is an organizational chart readily available which reflects the current structure and accurately identifies all components, positions and interrelationships?   _____

Function Statements

* Are documented functional statements available for all components which define roles and authority, and completely describe all responsibilities?   _____

Job Descriptions

* Are job descriptions available for each basic position and specific descriptions prepared for each position with special or individual characteristics?   _____

* Has each employee been provided a copy of their job description, and are actions taken at least annually (e.g., performance evaluations) to ensure that each employee clearly understands his/her role and responsibilities?   _____

Active Updating Procedure

* Is an updating procedure in effect for organizational documentation, with specific responsibility assigned, and are updates made on a continuing basis as they occur?   _____

* Does the organization really operate in accordance with this documentation?   _____

Comments

A. Guideline Checklists

A-2 Policies, Rules, Services

General Policies

• Have physical plant mission, objectives and general policy statements been developed and documented? _____

Complete Policies

• Do personnel policies cover all appropriate subject areas and do they assure consistent and equitable treatment of all personnel? _____

• Have physical plant policies, rules, and standard procedures been documented and distributed to all personnel? _____

Complete Services

• Has the maintenance organization role, services, and interdepartmental relationships been clearly defined, documented, and distributed? _____

Active Updating Procedure

• Is there an updating procedure in effect for this documentation, with specific responsibility assigned, and are appropriate updates performed? _____

Comments

A. Guideline Checklists

A-3 Work Control (Functions)

Independent Work Control

- Has an independent work control unit been established within the maintenance organization? _____

Basic Work Control Responsibilities

- Do basic control functions assigned to this unit include: centralized work reception, facility condition inspection, planning and estimating, work order preparation and approval, shop load planning, technical support for long range maintenance planning and budgeting, project management, and contract administration? _____

Total Workload Management

- Is all work authorized for shop accomplishment processed through work control, and is work control responsible for overall work load management? _____

Overall Effectiveness Evaluation

- Has work control been assigned responsibilities for review and evaluation of overall workload and work accomplishment, with the objectives of enhancing productivity, quality, and overall operational effectiveness and economy? _____

Comments

Worksheet IV.3

39

A. Guideline Checklists

A-4 Work Control (Staffing)

(The following items are appropriate primarily for medium and larger size maintenance organizations. Delete the rating and target if not appropriate.)

Work Reception Training

• Is the work reception function staffed with personnel who are familiar with facilities maintenance practices, trained to obtain complete and accurate information, and capable of providing authoritative information? _____

Planning Staff

• Do technicians, planner-estimators and inspectors have craft experience, and training in estimating, inspection techniques, and preparation of work orders and contracts? Are the equivalent number of planner-estimators preparing work orders staffed at a ratio of at least 1 to 40 workers? _____

Inspection Staff

• Are the equivalent number of facility condition inspectors staffed at a ratio of at least 1 for every 2,000,000 gross square feet to provide the capability of completing facility inspections on a two-year cycle? _____

Management Analysis

• Has a management analyst position been established in work control and assigned an appropriate role? _____

Comments

A. Guideline Checklists

A-5 Shop Organization

Shop Functions

- Are the functions of each unit documented, and is assignment of responsibilities accompanied by the appropriate degree of authority? _____

Lines of Authority

- Are shop policies and rules documented, distributed and practiced? Are the lines of authority clear and distinct with a minimum of vertical levels between shop head and worker? _____

Related Crafts Relationships

- Are related craft functions grouped together to provide optimum flexibility in use of craft skills? _____

Effectiveness Evaluation

- Has the shop organization been reviewed for effectiveness during the past two years? Is shop organization centralized or decentralized? Have the specific advantages and disadvantages of each been identified and considered? Is emergency response capability adequately provided for? Are separate preventive maintenance and/or service call components established to provide more specialized and effective operations, if warranted, by organization size and workload characteristics? _____

Comments

Worksheet IV.5

41

A. Guideline Checklists

A-6 Shop Supervision and Planning Functions

Supervisory Ratios

* Is the overall ratio of supervisors to craft workers approximately 1 to 10? For each individual craft, is the ratio between the range of 1 to 5-15?   _____

Multicraft Job Coordination

* Does the organization provide for effective coordination and supervision of multicraft jobs?   _____

Supervisory Coverage

* Is adequate supervision provided during the absence of the assigned supervisor? Are supervisors provided on every shift that subordinate personnel are required to work? If not, how is supervisory responsibility for this work handled?   _____

Planning Functions

* Have shop planner and/or shop scheduling functions been established to support shop supervisors in the details of scheduling and coordinating work, procuring materials, facilitating the movement of personnel, recordkeeping, etc.?   _____

Comments

A. Guideline Checklists

B-1 Facility Inventory

Current Facility Inventory

- Is a current inventory of all facilities available? _____

General Data

- Is general inventory data documented, such as: Gross Square Feet (GSF), Net Assignable Square Feet (NASF)/user, Current Replacement Value (CRV), type of construction, age, etc.? Is this data current? _____

Detailed Data

- Is detailed inventory data documented, such as: list of building components and systems, including type of material, size, capacity, etc.? Is this data adequate and current? Is a current area map available with real estate boundaries, location of each facility, roads, walkways, parking lots, utility system layout, etc.? _____

Active Updating Procedure

- Is an updating procedure in effect with specific responsibilities assigned and are documents updated on a continuing basis as changes occur? _____

Comments

A. Guideline Checklists

B-2 Facility Condition Inspection (FCI)

The FCI is a planned and organized visual inspection performed by selected and trained personnel that will produce complete and quantitative reports of deficiencies, recommend maintenance priorities, and provide credible work planning and budget support data.

Scope of Inspection Defined

- Have all facilities been identified which are appropriate for inspection, with classifications for owned, leased, unoccupied, etc.? Are inspectors technically qualified and trained in inspection techniques and report preparation? _____

Inspection Schedule

- Have inspection schedules been established and documented to include facility identification number, week of inspection, and inspection time for each facility? Have appropriate frequencies for inspection been established for each facility based on condition and priority of use? Are all significant facilities inspected at least every three years? Do scheduled hours for each inspection match actual hours available for each inspection? Are checklists and inspection guides available, appropriate, and used? Are facility occupants advised in advance of inspections and encouraged to provide lists of deficiencies? Do inspection reports contain specific details of deficiencies, i.e., units, estimated costs, location in facility, priority, etc.? _____

Inspection Performance

- Are inspections accomplished within ± 10% of schedule? Is schedule performance documented, periodically reported to and reviewed by management? Do inspection reports for maintenance work flow to work scheduling, and do major projects go to capital budget planning? _____

Operations- and Maintenance-Funded Maintenance and Repairs

- Is a reasonable percentage of operations- and maintenance- (O&M) funded maintenance and repair work generated by the inspection program? Is management assured that a substantial portion of this work is identified and corrected during earlier stages of deterioration, before more advanced and costly deterioration and breakdowns occur? _____

Worksheet IV.8

44

A. Guideline Checklists

B-3 Work Request Procedure

Documented Procedure

- Is there a documented work request procedure with standard forms which define parameters for generation and submission? _____

Authorization Control

- Is there an established control on the authority of personnel who approve the issue of work requests? Are requests for alteration and improvement work approved by an authority higher than the maintenance organization? _____

Processing

- Are all work requests received at a central control point within the maintenance organization? Is there a consistent screening process and rationale for determining priorities and for granting approval to accomplish the work? _____

Feedback to Requestor

- Is periodic feedback information provided to the requestor, such as notice of receipt, planned action, status, etc.? _____

Comments

A. Guideline Checklists

B-4 Equipment Inventory

Current Equipment Inventory

- Is there a current inventory of facilities-related equipment?   _____

Detailed Data

- Is there an adequate and accurate level of detail recorded in the equipment inventory for each item of equipment, such as: classification, description, location, manufacturer information, size, capacities, system, etc.?   _____

Computerized Equipment Inventory

- Is the equipment inventory computerized with provisions for producing various sorts, such as: equipment class, manufacturer, location, shop, priority, etc.? Is the equipment inventory integrated with a preventive maintenance program?   _____

Active Updating Procedure

- Is an updating procedure in effect with specific responsibilities assigned, and are updates recorded on a continuing basis as they occur?   _____

Comments

Worksheet IV.10

A. Guideline Checklists

B-5 Preventive Maintenance (Equipment)

Preventive maintenance (PM) is defined in the maintenance management audit as periodically scheduled work on selected equipment, usually dynamic, to provide for required inspection, lubrication and adjustment. In order to maintain the schedule, it does not include time for repairs or replacements which are authorized separately.

Procedures Established

* Have all facilities-related equipment items appropriate to PM been identified? Have equipment PM standards been prepared for each item to include: checkpoints, frequency of inspection, and time required to inspect? _____

Work Orders Issued and Personnel Assigned

* Do work orders prepared and issued to authorize PM work list all work items, identify check-points, and cite time to accomplish? Are personnel assigned to PM technically qualified and trained? Are definite limits set and adhered to for the amount of PM time allowed for making adjustments or repairs? Is provision made for recording results of each PM for each checkpoint? Are problems identified by PM promptly reported and acted on? _____

* Has specific responsibility for operator-performed PM been documented within standard operating procedures? Has an annual PM plan and weekly PM schedule been established, and are they consistent with the shop hours available to assign to this work? _____

Preventive Maintenance Work Performance

* Is PM work accomplished within 10% of schedule? Is PM schedule performance documented and periodically reported to and reviewed by management? _____

Equipment Records

* Are equipment history records maintained and periodically reviewed for general condition, cost trends, downtime, replacement requirements, etc.? Do these records automatically flag problem items? _____

Worksheet IV.11

A. Guideline Checklists

B-6 Service Work

Service work is defined as small, single-craft jobs which require less than four hours each to complete. These jobs are generally not appropriate for scheduling individually and should be processed differently from other types of work. Also, because of its nature, service work tends to be considerably less productive than other types of work and therefore should be minimized to the fullest extent possible.

Service Work Classification

- Is service type work classified and processed separately from other types of work? _____

Service Work Authorization

- Is there an established and documented control on the authority of personnel in requesting activities to approve initiation of service work? _____

Processing Procedures

- Are all service requests received at a central control point within the maintenance organization? Is there a consistent screening process and rationale for determining priorities and approval to accomplish? Are time limit targets established and adhered to for completion of Service Orders based on priority? Is a suspense (on-hold status) system maintained to provide frequent follow-up on uncompleted service work? Is feedback information provided to requestor regarding status of service orders? _____

Workload Analysis

- What is the average percentage of the total work force assigned to service work? Are there policies to balance staff workload between service work and other maintenance assignments? _____

Comments

A. Guideline Checklists

B-7 Routine, Recurring Work

Routine, recurring work is defined in this application as work which is repetitive and for which expended time and costs are accumulated on standing work orders. Examples are: relamping, maintenance of kitchen equipment, tool maintenance, sign making, pest control, etc. Have all routine, recurring work responsibilities of the maintenance organization been identified and documented?

Recurring Work Classification

- Is routine, recurring work classified and controlled separately from other types of work? Have standing work orders been written for each recurring function or task? _____

Standing Work Order Specification

- Do standing work orders include the following information: description of work, frequency and/or dates, number and hours of shifts, estimated labor, material and equipment costs? Are the hours planned on each work order consistent with the shop hours available to assign to this work? _____

Standing Work Order Scheduling

- Are standing work orders scheduled weekly and accomplished within $\pm$ 10% of schedule? _____

Standing Work Order Performance Reporting

- Is standing work order performance within $\pm$ 10% of scheduled hours documented and periodically reported to and reviewed by management? _____

Comments

Worksheet IV.13

A. Guideline Checklists

B-8 Work Requirements Documentation

Work Requirement Documentation

- Is a complete list of all known work requirements (maintenance and repair deficiencies) compiled and maintained in such a form that it is readily available for management review and for overall workload planning? _____

Prioritization

- Have all work items been prioritized and quantified with at least preliminary craft hour and cost estimates? Can these work requirements be readily sorted and summarized by requestor, fund source, type of work and priority? _____

Summaries of Status

- Can these work requirements be identified and summarized by status (i.e., deferred, in planning, waiting material, scheduled start and complete dates, etc.)? _____

Workload Review

- Is workload reviewed periodically to identify bottlenecks and shortfalls or to project potential problem areas? Is feedback on status provided to appropriate sources? _____

Comments

A. Guideline Checklists

C-1 Priority Criteria

Criteria Established, Documented and Distributed

- Has a priority criteria been established, documented and distributed to maintenance planners, supervisors, and customers? _____

Criteria Appropriateness

- Does the priority criteria address factors such as safety, regulatory compliance, energy conservation, economic payback, mission or functional requirements? _____

Consistent Application

- Is the priority criteria applied consistently to all work? _____

Review Procedure

- Is completed work recorded and summarized by priority, to determine work force distribution and amount of backlog on various priorities? Is this information reported to planning and management periodically? _____

Comments

A. Guideline Checklists

C-2 Work Classification

Classification Definitions

- Is all work formally classified to distinguish between very small jobs (service orders), larger one-time jobs (specific work orders) and routine, recurring work (standing work orders)?   _____

Work Processing Procedures

- Have procedures for processing work been developed, documented and implemented which are tailored to the special characteristics of each class of work? Are these procedures consistently applied?   _____

Work force Distribution

- Have planning targets been established for optimum distribution of the work force to each class of work?   _____

Review Procedure

- Is completed work recorded and summarized by class of work and used by management and planning as a means to evaluate work force utilization?   _____

Comments

A. Guideline Checklists

C-3 Alteration and Improvement (A/I) Work

Alteration and improvement work is defined in this application as work which consists primarily of changing or upgrading a facility configuration or component, usually generated by functional or regulatory requirements.

Classification Definitions

- Is alteration and improvement work identified separately from maintenance and repair work? Are approval and priority levels for alteration and improvement work established by an authority above the maintenance organization management? Is all alteration and improvement work processed by work control? _____

Processing Procedures

- Is a significant percentage of alteration and improvement work funded by the requestor or by a source separate from maintenance and repair budget? _____

Work Programming

- Is a significant percentage of alteration and improvement work allocated sufficient lead time to provide for orderly planning and scheduling? _____

Work force Distribution

- What is the average percentage of the work force applied to alteration and improvement work? Is this within a preplanned target range? What is the average percentage of operating and maintenance funds expended on alteration and improvement work? Is this within the preplanned budget? _____

Comments

Worksheet IV.17

A. Guideline Checklists

C-4 Work Order Preparation

Work Order Information

- Is all work authorized for shop accomplishment documented on appropriate work order or service order forms?   _____

Detailed Information

- Is the work description complete enough to minimize worker planning time and to clearly define the limits of work authorized for accomplishment? Is authority to approve work orders clearly assigned? Do all work orders have an estimate of hours and costs? Are engineered performance standards used consistently and accurately as the principal basis for hourly estimates? Is the job priority identified on each work order?   _____

Job Phasing

- Are larger jobs analyzed, planned, described, and estimated by job phase?   _____

Material Requirement

- Are material lists provided, and special equipment or other special requirements identified on the work order?   _____

Comments

A. Guideline Checklists

C-5 Budget Requirements for Annual Maintenance and Repair (M&R) Budget

Budgetary Methods

- How are maintenance and repair funding requirement amounts derived for use in planning the annual operating and maintenance budget for the maintenance organization? Are these amounts based primarily on past budget levels or on a fixed formula approach? _____

Cost Reporting

- Does the recording of annual operating and maintenance expenditures provide an accurate indication of the amounts spent on minor maintenance and repair work separate from minor alterations, improvements and incidental services? What is the percentage of total operating and maintenance funds that are expended on maintenance and repair? Is there an indication that maintenance and repair work is being subordinated to other types of work? _____

Budget Documentation

- During the budget planning process, are the unfunded maintenance and repair requirements quantified, documented, and provided to approval authorities, accompanied by an explanation of shortfalls, impacts, etc.? Are provisions made in the budget process to identify maintenance and repair requirements to support new construction and to increase the operating and maintenance budget base for this purpose? _____

Long-Range Requirement

- Have long range requirements for building component renewal and replacement been identified and presented formally to financial and policy managers; and have commitments been made to provide ongoing funding for this purpose? _____

Comments

Worksheet IV.19

55

A. Guideline Checklists

C-6 Backlog of Deferred Maintenance and Repair

Backlog Reporting

- The backlog of deferred maintenance and repair consists of the accumulated total of facility condition deficiencies which have been deferred, primarily due to lack of funds in annual budget cycles. Has the backlog of deferred maintenance and repair been compiled during the past 12 months? _____

Inspections

- Was this amount developed as the result of on-site inspections of all significant facilities during the past two years? Is this amount updated at least annually by adding inflation cost to uncompleted backlog, deleting completed work, and adding newly found deficiencies? _____

Backlog Analysis

- Are the past year's backlog amounts and trends recorded and reported? Are these amounts and trends categorized to provide more effective evaluations, for example, by type of facility, cost center, location? _____

Backlog Reduction Plan

- What is the percentage of backlog as it relates to current replacement value? Is the overall condition of facilities considered good, fair or poor? Has a target backlog amount been established and is there a formal plan for reducing backlog to the target level? _____

Comments

A. Guideline Checklists

C-7 Budget Execution Plan

Budget Execution Planning

- Is there a budget execution plan established on a monthly or quarterly basis that identifies planned expenditure amounts by categories or accounts within each fund source? _____

Budget Classification

- Does this plan include breakdowns by *object class*, such as salaries, fringe benefits, materials, training; and by *end use*, such as maintenance and repair, alteration and improvement? _____

Work Item Definition

- Are specific work items identified individually in the budget execution plan? What percentage of total in-house hours on specific work items were applied to items identified on the plan? _____

Budget Controls

- Is an adequate procedure established to control expenditures against these plans? Are actual expenditures reported periodically and compared with the plan? Is performance generally within ± 10% of the plan? Is a careful evaluation of performance against the plan made at the end of the accounting period? Was performance acceptable? Were problems identified and actions taken to improve this performance during subsequent periods? _____

Comments

A. Guideline Checklists

C-8 Backlog of Funded Work

Backlog Definition

- Is there an accepted and applied definition for work backlog? Is the backlog of approved and funded work documented, summarized periodically by funding source, and reported to management? _____

Backlog Summaries

- Is the backlog of approved and funded work summarized periodically by priority, type of work or by shop? _____

Backlog Reviews

- Are backlog reports listing approved and funded work reviewed periodically to identify existing problem areas (such as bottlenecks or shortfalls)? Are corrective actions being taken? _____

Backlog Analysis

- Are the backlog reports reviewed periodically for trends to project (1) potential problems and (2) take actions to avoid those problems? _____

Comments

A. Guideline Checklists

D-1 Shop Planning and Scheduling Procedures

Scheduling Established

- Has a weekly scheduling procedure been developed and documented which identifies and plans the individual work orders and hours to be worked by each shop? Are all shop hours accounted for?　　　　　　　　　_____

Scheduling Procedures

- Are schedule/progress meetings held each week to ensure understanding, agreement, and coordination? Do the maintenance organization manager and shop head participate actively in the scheduling process? Is responsibility for schedule preparation assigned, and is adequate time available for preparation of the weekly schedule? Is feedback from the shops on work accomplished prompt and accurate?　　　　_____

Scheduling Performance

- Is scheduling performance within $\pm$ 10%? If not, are the causes objectively identified and prompt corrective actions taken?　　　　　　　　　_____

Shop Planning Support

- Is shop planning support available for material ordering, staging and delivery to work site, and for arranging transportation, equipment, work site availability, etc.?　　　　_____

Comments

A. Guideline Checklists

D-2 Craft and Material Availability

Craft Distribution Planning

- Is the distribution of the shop work force planned weekly as the basis for the weekly shop schedule? Does this plan identify shop hours planned for leave and overhead and allocate remaining hours to each class of work? _____

Work Order Scheduling

- Are work orders scheduled only when craft hours are planned to be available? _____

Material Scheduling

- Is the availability of material and equipment required for individual work orders identified prior to scheduling? Are the principal materials for individual large jobs procured and reserved prior to start of work on the job? _____

Material Availability

- Are work orders scheduled only when materials and equipment are available? _____

Comments

A. Guideline Checklists

D-3 Training Program

Training on an Unstructured Basis

- Is any training being provided to supervisors and workers this year? _____

Formal Training

- Is there a formal training program for supervisors and workers with adequate funding each year? Are personnel receptive and active in seeking self-improvement? _____

Needs Assessment Reviews

- Are training assignments based on a *needs assessment review* which considers capabilities of individuals and projected future needs of the organization? Are supervisors trained in human relations, work simplification and cost reduction techniques, new equipment, tools, methods and materials? Has an active follow-up effort been performed to achieve and identify actual benefits from this training? _____

Apprentice Program

- Is there an active formal apprentice program? _____

Comments

A. Guideline Checklists

D-4 Shop Spaces, Tools, Equipment

Shop Adequacy

- Does shop location (area, zone, central, etc.) permit the most efficient use of the work force; for example, is excessive time lost going to and from shops to work sites or storage areas? Are general shop features adequate, such as size, layout, lighting, heating, ventilation, office area, toilet/locker facilities, storage? _____

Tools and Equipment

- Is shop equipment adequate to procure first class workmanship, available enough to minimize wait-time, and maintained in safe and top working condition? Is there a tool control system with accountability? Are the quantity and type of tools adequate? Do workers use inferior methods because of inferior tools? Do workers lose time waiting for tools and equipment? _____

Budgeting

- Is there an adequate annual budget for replacement and upgrading of shop tools and equipment? _____

Shop Conditions

- Are shop facilities consistently well maintained with good housekeeping practices in effect on a continuing basis? _____

Comments

A. Guideline Checklists

D-5 Storeroom Operation

Storeroom Security

- Is there an adequate and secure shop store and warehouse within or readily available to the shops?

Procedure and Record Systems

- Have instructions been developed which include records, controls, and procedures for material ordering, expediting, notification of receipt, and withdrawal? Are these procedures followed consistently? Is a record of number of items *on-hand* and *reserved* maintained currently? Are historical usage rates compiled and monitored? Have order points been established and used consistently? Has detailed vendor information been compiled, including costs and substitution data?

Salvage and "Bench Stock" Controls

- Is there a continuing and effective salvage and reclamation program integrated with inventory control? Is there an excessive amount of unaccounted and uncontrolled "bench stock"?

Management Information

- What summary data, such as: work waiting on materials, procurement times, turnover rates, stock outage records, etc., is periodically compiled and reviewed by management? What is the value of the maintenance stores inventory? Has a target range been established for this investment?

Comments

Worksheet IV.27

A. Guideline Checklists

D-6 Transportation

Adequacy

- Is adequate transportation available to move personnel and materials to job sites?   _____

Operation and Maintenance

- Are assignments of vehicles to shops or individuals adequately controlled, with responsibilities for operation and maintenance fully established? Are vehicles operated and maintained appropriately?   _____

Tools and Equipment

- Are vehicles configured and equipped with adequate tools and materials to facilitate field work and to minimize extra travel to shop and store areas?   _____

Utilization Reporting

- Is vehicle utilization monitored to ensure efficient and economical operation? Are vehicle replacement requirements identified and programmed in the budget process?   _____

Comments

Worksheet IV.28

64

A. Guideline Checklists

D-7 Supervisory Practices

Direct Supervision

• What percentage of supervisory time is spent on direct supervision and nonsupervisory work? Is this adequate? What nonsupervisory work does each supervisor perform? Is this a problem and what can be done to minimize it?   _____

Supervisory Training Program

• Has a continuing and effective supervisory training program been established to cover organization policies and procedures, personnel administration, supervisory practices and craft-oriented new techniques, materials, tools, etc.?   _____

Supervisory Responsibilities

• Are supervisors held accountable for quality of work by certifying that completed work has been accomplished satisfactorily? Are supervisors responsible for evaluating work performance and identifying and documenting causes for excessive variances between planned and actual schedules, hours, costs, etc.? Are supervisors encouraged to offer suggestions for maintenance and operations cost savings?   _____

Training and Safety Programs

• Do supervisors actively identify worker's training needs and encourage career development? Do supervisors actively support the safety program; attend, participate and/or conduct safety meetings?   _____

Comments

Worksheet IV.29

A. Guideline Checklists

D-8 Use of Contracts

Balancing Contracts and In-house Staff

- What percentage of maintenance and repair work is accomplished by contract? Does this provide a good balance with in-house forces?   _____

Contract Administration

- Are contracts prepared and administered by personnel who are experienced and trained? Are contracts' legal and technical provisions prepared appropriately?   _____

Contract Performance

- Is performance of contractors monitored and recorded in accordance with a formal quality assurance plan?   _____

Management Evaluation

- Are formal evaluations and cost comparisons made between contract and in-house performance?   _____

Comments

A. Guideline Checklists

E-1 Management Information System (MIS)

MIS Adequacy

- Has the maintenance organization established a basic MIS with a set of management reports which are compiled and distributed at least monthly? _____

Report Design

- Are these reports designed for use by management and supervision at all levels? For example, do they include detail information regarding the operation? Are they structured for use by planners and shop supervisors, and summarized for management use? _____

Facility and Equipment Reports

- Does the MIS also include provision for compiling historic data for facilities and equipment? _____

Report Utilization

- Are reports generated by the MIS reviewed, evaluated, and discussed periodically in management meetings? Are actions taken to improve the overall operation as a result of these reviews? _____

Comments

A. Guideline Checklists

E-2 Performance Measurement

Performance Measurement Methods

- How is shop work performance measured? Are estimates of hours and costs made for each specific and recurring work order? Are estimated and actual hours, and costs on work orders tabulated and reported periodically to supervision and management? _____

Report Summaries

- Are these tabulations sorted and summarized by shop and by class of work? Is performance against targets reported for work force distribution, work scheduling, priority, and backlog reduction? _____

Engineered Performance Standards

- Are engineered performance standards used as the basis for estimates of labor hours on work orders? _____

Improvement Studies

- Has a work methods improvement study been conducted during the past two years with emphasis on improving the performance of craft work? _____

Comments

A. Guideline Checklists

E-3 Productivity Measurement

Productivity is defined in a maintenance management audit as the percentage of the workday which is applied *directly* to accomplishing an assigned task (such as measuring and cutting a board). It does not include indirect activities (such as traveling to job or clean-up) or non-productive time (such as waiting or personal time).

Productivity Study Frequency

- Are productivity measures used to evaluate the effectiveness of the work force? Has a productivity study of the shop work force been conducted within the past two years? _____

Work Sampling

- Did this study include a statistically valid work sampling of at least a representative portion of the shop work force? _____

Comparisons

- Did the work sampling study identify various categories of work, quantify the percentage of time spent on each category and compare results with established targets? _____

Improvement Action Plan

- In addition to quantifying productivity, did this study provide insights on day-to-day shop practices which may be impeding full productivity; and if so, have improvement actions been initiated? _____

Comments

Worksheet IV.33

A. Guideline Checklists

E-4 Variance Reviews

Variance Review Policy

- What are current practices for identifying and reviewing variances between planned and actual activities? Has a specific policy been established to identify and evaluate selected variances which are reported through the management information system? _____

Review Responsibilities

- Does this policy assign specific lead and support responsibilities for this review? Does it establish parameters which define subjects and guidelines for conducting these reviews? _____

Supervisory Review

- Are supervisors instructed to follow progress on all jobs, to project and note impending variances, and to take action to prevent or minimize variances? _____

Variance Records

- Are records made of the circumstances of significant variances and periodically reviewed to reduce recurrence? _____

Comments

A. Guideline Checklists

E-5 Facility History Records

Work Order Records

- Are facility history records maintained of all work performed on each facility? In what form (completed work order files, manual tabulations, computerized database)? _____

Record Data

- Do these records include descriptions and date of work accomplished in each facility, along with a record of in-house or contract costs? Are they current within two months? _____

Summaries

- Is the cost of completed work summarized periodically for each facility by type of work (service, maintenance and repair, alterations and improvement, etc.) and/or by component (roof, floor, heating system, etc.)? Is this summary data tabulated and structured in a format that facilitates timely and comparative evaluation of work performed and costs? _____

Quarterly Analyses

- Are facility history records reviewed at least quarterly for indications of recurring problems and/or excessive costs, etc. _____

Comments

A. Guideline Checklists

E-6 Equipment History Records

Individual Equipment Records

- Are equipment history records established for each piece of equipment? In what form (completed work order files, manual tabulations, computerized database)? _____

Equipment Work Records

- Do these records provide a list of all work accomplished on each piece of equipment, along with planned and actual hours and costs? Are they current within two months? _____

Work Summaries

- Are summaries provided for each piece of equipment to identify current and projected condition, accumulated hours and costs for current year, and overall life of the item? _____

Analyses

- Are equipment history records reviewed periodically to identify indications of recurring problems and/or excessive costs? _____

Comments

Worksheet IV.36

A. Guideline Checklists

E-7 Trend Data

Trend Data Compilation

- Is trend data developed from information in the MIS? _____

Operational Trends

- Does this data include shorter range/monthly trends of operational performance against targets for work order hours and costs, work force distribution, work scheduling, priorities, etc.? Is this data reported by operational unit or shop? _____

Long Range Trends

- Does this data include longer range/annual trends for actual maintenance and repair funding levels compared with reported requirements, backlog of deferred maintenance, alterations and improvements, new construction, square feet maintained, current replacement value, etc.? Is this data reported by cost center, type of facility, area or location? _____

Management Reviews

- Are trend lines charted, reported periodically, and provided to management and all operational units? Are these data utilized in the establishment of goals and targets and in identifying potential problem areas which may require special attention? _____

Comments

Worksheet IV.37

B. Effectiveness Rating Worksheet

A. Organization

		RATING		TARGET
1.	**Organization (Structure)**	7 x ___		28
	Documentation not prepared or outdated	0		
	Organization Chart	1		
	Functional Statements	1		
	Job Descriptions	1		
	Active Updating Procedure	1		
2.	**Policies, Rules, Services**	7 x ___		28
	Documentation not prepared or outdated	0		
	General policies, rules written	1		
	Complete policies, rules written, distributed	1		
	Complete services, written, distributed	1		
	Active updating procedure	1		
3.	**Work Control (Functions)**	9 x ___		36
	Independent work control function not established	0		
	Independent work control function established	1		
	All basic work control responsibilities assigned	1		
	Process and manage total workload	1		
	Overview evaluation for effectiveness	1		
4.	**Work Control (Staffing)**	8 x ___		32
	Clerical only	0		
	Work Reception, trained	1		
	Planning Staff: adequate, trained	1		
	Inspection Staff: adequate, trained	1		
	Management analysis function	1		
5.	**Shop Organization**	5 x ___		20
	Documentation not prepared or outdated	0		
	Shop functions, policies, rules documented, distributed	1		
	Lines of authority clear, minimum vertical levels	1		
	Related crafts grouped together	1		
	Organization reviewed for effectiveness, past two years	1		

Worksheet IV.38

B. Effectiveness Rating Worksheet

A. Organization

			RATING	TARGET
6.	**Shop Supervision and Planning (Functions)**	6 x __		24
	Documentation not prepared or outdated	0		
	Supervisory ratios appropriate	1		
	Coordination of multi-craft jobs	1		
	Supervisory Coverage: shifts, others	1		
	Planning functions established	1		
	Additional Comments			
	TOTAL POINTS			168
	PERCENTAGE			

Worksheet IV.38 (cont.)

B. Effectiveness Rating Worksheet

B. Workload Identification

			RATING	TARGET
1.	**Facilities Inventory**	5 x __		20
	Records not prepared or outdated	0		
	Current facility list — general data incomplete	1		
	Current facility list — general data complete	1		
	Current facility list — detail data complete	1		
	Active Updating Procedure	1		
2.	**Facility Condition Inspection**	9 x __		36
	No structured function	0		
	Scope of inspection established and personnel available	1		
	Schedule established and inspections accomplished	1		
	Inspections accomplished ± 10% of schedule	1		
	Generate major portion of O&M-funded M&R	1		
3.	**Work Request Procedure**	4 x __		16
	Procedure not documented or outdated	0		
	Procedure documented and distributed	1		
	Authorization controlled	1		
	Structured processing	1		
	Status feedback provided to requestor	1		
4.	**Equipment Inventory**	5 x __		20
	Records not prepared or outdated	0		
	Current equipment list — detail data incomplete	1		
	Current equipment list — detail data complete	1		
	Current equipment list — computerized	1		
	Active updating procedure	1		
5.	**Preventive Maintenance (Equipment)**	6 x __		24
	No structured procedure	0		
	Procedure established, includes hours, frequency, schedule	1		
	Work Orders issued and personnel assigned	1		
	PM accomplished ± 10% of schedule	1		
	Equipment records maintained, reviewed	1		

Worksheet IV.39

B. Effectiveness Rating Worksheet

B. Workload Identification

RATING TARGET

6.	**Service Work**	6 x __			24
	Not classified separately from other types of work	0			
	Classified separately, unconstrained approval	1			
	Controlled approval, priorities identified	1			
	Structured processing procedure	1			
	Service workload analyzed, actions to reduce	1			
7.	**Routine, Recurring Work**	6 x __			24
	Not classified separately from other work	0			
	Classified separately, Work Order with general specifications	1			
	Work Order specifications quantified	1			
	Work Orders scheduled weekly in accordance with planned hours available	1			
	Work accomplished $\pm$ 10% of schedule	1			
8.	**Work Requirements Documentation**	7 x __			28
	Records not complete or readily accessible	0			
	Available but not summarized or quantifed	1			
	Quantified and summarized by requestor, priority	1			
	Summarized by status	1			
	Periodic workload review, feedback of status	1			
	Additional Comments				
	TOTAL POINTS			192
	PERCENTAGE			

Worksheet IV.39 (cont.)

B. Effectiveness Rating Worksheet

C. Workload Planning

			RATING	TARGET
1.	**Priority Criteria**	7 x __		28
	No formal priority criteria established	0		
	Priority criteria established and documented	1		
	Priority criteria addresses appropriate factors	1		
	Priority criteria applied consistently to all work	1		
	Work performance recorded by priority and reviewed	1		
2.	**Work Classification**	7 x __		28
	Work is not classified by type of authorization	0		
	Classification definitions established and documented	1		
	Processing procedures are tailored to each class of work	1		
	Workforce distribution targets for each class of work	1		
	Work performance recorded by class of work and reviewed	1		
3.	**Alteration and Improvement (A/I) Work Approval**	5 x __		20
	A/I work is not identified separately from M&R work	0		
	All A/I work processed by work control	1		
	A/I fund source separated from M&R	1		
	A/I work programmed with sufficient lead time	1		
	Level of A/I work within ± 10% planned workforce distribution	1		
4.	**Work Order (WO) Preparation**	10 x __		40
	Written W.O. not prepared for all work	0		
	W.O. issued, general description, no estimate	1		
	W.O. includes detail description with estimated hours and costs	1		
	W.O. planned by job phase	1		
	Material lists prepared	1		
5.	**Budget Requirements for Maintenance & Repair**	7 x __		28
	Based primarily on past budget amounts	0		
	Based primarily on a formula approach	1		
	Identifies total actual requirements	1		
	Provides valid documented justification	1		
	Identifies long-range requirements	1		

Worksheet IV.40

B. Effectiveness Rating Worksheet

C. Workload Planning		RATING	TARGET

6.	**Backlog of Deferred Maintenance & Repair**	6 x __			24
	Not compiled or updated past 12 months	0			
	Compiled/updated past 12 months	1			
	Based on on-site condition inspection past 2 years	1			
	Funds charted and evaluated	1			
	Backlog reduction plan established	1			
7.	**Budget Execution Plan**	5 x __			20
	Execution plans not documented	0			
	Execution plan documented, month/greater	1			
	Plan identifies "classes"/"types" of work	1			
	Plan identifies specific work items	1			
	Execution controlled against plan, ± 10%	1			
8.	**Backlog of Funded Work**	5 x __			20
	Not compiled or reported periodically	0			
	Totals computed and reported monthly	1			
	Summarized by fund source, priority, shop	1			
	Reviewed periodically	1			
	Trends compiled and analyzed	1			
	Additional Comments				
	TOTAL POINTS				208
	PERCENTAGE				

Worksheet IV.40 (cont.)

B. Effectiveness Rating Worksheet

D. Work Accomplishment

			RATING	TARGET
1.	**Shop Planning and Scheduling Procedures**	8 x __		32
	Formal functions not established	0		
	Scheduling functions established	1		
	Formal schedule procedures and planning accomplished weekly	1		
	Scheduling performance within ± 10%	1		
	Shop planning support provided	1		
2.	**Craft and Material Availability**	6 x __		24
	W.O. assigned without hour or material plan	0		
	Shop force distribution planned each week	1		
	W.O. scheduled only when craft hours are available	1		
	W.O. scheduled only when materials available	1		
	Principal materials procured and reserved	1		
3.	**Training Program**	6 x __		24
	Minimum interest indicated	0		
	Some training accomplished on unstructured basis	1		
	Training plan established and budgeted	1		
	Training plans based on needs assessment reviews	1		
	Active apprentice program	1		
4.	**Shop Spaces, Tools, Equipment**	7 x __		28
	Shop size, facilities, location inadequate	0		
	Shop size, location adequate	1		
	Shop tools, equipment adequate	1		
	Annual budget for shop replenishment	1		
	Good shop maintenance and housekeeping practices	1		
5.	**Storeroom Operation**	6 x __		24
	Limited security, accessibility, control	0		
	Secure and accessible to shops area	1		
	Control procedure and record systems established	1		
	Salvage activities and "bench-stock" adequately controlled	1		
	Operating information compiled for management use	1		

Worksheet IV.41

B. Effectiveness Rating Worksheet

D. Work Accomplishment

			RATING	TARGET
6.	**Transportation**	5 x __		20
	Inadequate, uncontrolled	0		
	Adequate number of vehicles available	1		
	Operation and maintenance controlled	1		
	Vehicles adequately equipped	1		
	Vehicle utilization monitored and replacements programmed			
7.	**Supervisory Practices**	7 x __		28
	Insufficient time and attention to direct supervision	0		
	Percent supervisory time on direct supervision is adequate	1		
	Effective supervisory training program	1		
	Supervisory responsibilities firmly established	1		
	Supervisors actively support workers' programs; training, safety, etc.	1		
8.	**Use of Contracts**	8 x __		32
	Use of contracts is insufficient or excessive	0		
	Reasonable balance between in-house and contract	1		
	Contract specialist function established and staffed	1		
	Contractor performance monitored with a formal QA plan	1		
	Management evaluation of use of contracts	1		
	Additional Comments			
	TOTAL POINTS			212
	PERCENTAGE			

Worksheet IV.41 (cont.)

B. Effectiveness Rating Worksheet

E. Appraisal

			RATING	TARGET
1.	**Management Information System (MIS)**	8x __		32
	No structured system, inadequate/untimely reports	0		
	Basic system established with monthly reports	1		
	Reports specifically designed for each user level	1		
	System includes facility and equipment history records	1		
	Reports utilized extensively at all user levels	1		
2.	**Performance Measurement**	6 x __		24
	No effective measure of performance established	0		
	Estimated and actual hours/costs reported each W.O.	1		
	Performance data summarized and reported against targets	1		
	Engineered Performance Standards used as basis for W.O. estimates	1		
	Methods improvement studies conducted during past two years	1		
3.	**Productivity Measurement**	6 x __		24
	Not studied/measured during past two years	0		
	Productivity study accomplished during past two years	1		
	Productivity study included valid work sampling	1		
	Work sampling measured work categories & compared with established targets	1		
	Study results generated an improvement action plan	1		
4.	**Variance Reviews**	6 x __		24
	Not accomplished as a routine practice	0		
	Policy established and implemented for variance reviews	1		
	Policy assigns responsibilities and parameters	1		
	Supervisors review work-in-progress to identify variances	1		
	Are variance records maintained and reviewed	1		
5.	**Facility History Records**	6 x __		24
	Not established	0		
	Records consist primarily of completed W.O. files	1		
	Records contain adequate and current data	1		
	Data summarized and structured for review and evaluation	1		
	Analyzed quarterly	1		

Worksheet IV.42

B. Effectiveness Rating Worksheet

E. Appraisal

			RATING	TARGET
6.	**Equipment History Records**	6 x __		24
	Not established	0		
	Records established for each piece of equipment	1		
	Records contain adequate and current data	1		
	Data summarized and structured for review and evaluation	1		
	Analyzed periodically as routine practice	1		
7.	**Trend Data**	7 x __		28
	Not compiled	0		
	Compiled on occasional or irregular basis	1		
	Includes operational trends by performing unit	1		
	Includes longer range departmental trends	1		
	Charted routinely, major factor in overall management appraisal	1		
	Additional Comments			
	TOTAL POINTS			180
	PERCENTAGE			

Worksheet IV.42 (cont.)

C. Effectiveness Rating Summary

	CURRENT RATING	TARGET
A. Organization		
1. Organization (Structure)	_____	_____
2. Policies, Rules, Services	_____	_____
3. Work Control Center (Functions)	_____	_____
4. Work Control Center (Staffing)	_____	_____
5. Shop Organization	_____	_____
6. Shop Supervision & Planning (Functions)	_____	_____
B. Workload Identification		
1. Facilities Inventory	_____	_____
2. Facility Condition Inspection	_____	_____
3. Work Request Procedure	_____	_____
4. Equipment Inventory	_____	_____
5. Preventive Maintenance (Equipment)	_____	_____
6. Service Work	_____	_____
7. Routine, Recurring Work	_____	_____
8. Work Requirements Documentation	_____	_____
C. Work Planning		
1. Priority Criteria	_____	_____
2. Work Classification	_____	_____
3. Alterations & Improvement (A/I) Work — Approval	_____	_____
4. Work Order (WO) Preparation	_____	_____
5. Budget Requirements for M&R	_____	_____
6. Backlog Deferred Maintenance & Repair	_____	_____
7. Budget Execution Plan	_____	_____
8. Backlog of Funded Work	_____	_____
D. Work Accomplishment		
1. Shop Scheduling & Planning Procedures	_____	_____
2. Craft and Material Availability	_____	_____
3. Training Program	_____	_____
4. Shop Spaces, Tools, Equipment	_____	_____
5. Storeroom Operation	_____	_____
6. Transportation	_____	_____
7. Supervisory Practices	_____	_____
8. Use of Contracts	_____	_____
E. Appraisal		
1. Management Information System (MIS)	_____	_____
2. Performance Measurement	_____	_____
3. Productivity Measurement	_____	_____
4. Variance Reviews	_____	_____
5. Facility History Records	_____	_____
6. Equipment History Records	_____	_____
7. Trend Data	_____	_____
TOTAL POINTS		
PERCENTAGE RATING		

Worksheet IV.43

Part Five
Case Study

Part Five
Case Study

This case study is based on a Maintenance Management Audit conducted at a major university during the period December 1-5, 1990. It shows examples of actual results to illustrate the process outlined in this book. Since this audit was performed by the authors in their role as outside consultants, the case study starts with the process outlined in Part III of this book. See Part IV for all of the forms referred to in the case study.

Profile of Audited Facility

The university reviewed in the case study is comprised of 2.5 million square feet. There are approximately 125 employees in the Facilities Maintenance Department. The university consists of a single campus located in a "college town." The shops area is centrally located, with each building having only an expanded janitorial closet and a designated building manager. The on-site building manager is responsible for maintaining a running requirements list, such that all work orders issued by that building are dispatched from that office. The audit of the Physical Plant Department did not involve interviews with the individual building managers since they were not part of the Maintenance Department organizationally.

The audit centered on personnel and procedures based on guidance from the university's Board of Regents.

Preliminary Program Review

The first step was the Preliminary Program Review, which used the Guideline Checklists as the basic outline for the study.

While the reviewer completed all the checklists before proceeding to the next steps, only the checklist for the "Organization" component is shown here (Figure V.1), as an example of how these forms are used.

Effectiveness Rating

The next step was to complete the Effectiveness Rating Worksheets, using the information compiled on the Guideline Checklists during the Preliminary Program Review. The completed Effectiveness Rating Worksheets and the Effectiveness Rating Summary for the case study are shown in Figures V.2 and V.3. All of the forms—the Guideline Checklists, the Worksheets, and the Summary were compiled in accordance with the instructions detailed in Part III.

A. Guideline Checklists

A-1 Organization (Structure)

Organization Chart

- Is an organizational chart readily available which reflects the current structure and accurately identifies all components, positions and interrelationships?　　　Y

Function Statements

- Are documented functional statements available for all components which define roles and authority, and completely describe all responsibilities?　　　N

Job Descriptions

- Are job descriptions available for each basic position and specific descriptions prepared for each position with special or individual characteristics?　　　N

- Has each employee been provided a copy of their job description, and are actions taken at least annually (e.g., performance evaluations) to ensure that each employee clearly understands his/her role and responsibilities?　　　N

Active Updating Procedure

- Is an updating procedure in effect for organizational documentation, with specific responsibility assigned, and are updates made on a continuing basis as they occur?　　　N

- Does the organization really operate in accordance with this documentation?　　　P

Comments

Figure V.1

A. Guideline Checklists

A-2 Policies, Rules, Services

General Policies

- Have physical plant mission, objectives and general policy statements been developed and documented? <u> Y </u>

Complete Policies

- Do personnel policies cover all appropriate subject areas and do they assure consistent and equitable treatment of all personnel? <u> Y </u>

- Have physical plant policies, rules, and standard procedures been documented and distributed to all personnel? <u> Y </u>

Complete Services

- Has the maintenance organization role, services, and interdepartmental relationships been clearly defined, documented, and distributed? <u> Y </u>

Active Updating Procedure

- Is there an updating procedure in effect for this documentation, with specific responsibility assigned, and are appropriate updates performed? <u> Y </u>

Comments

Figure V.1 (cont.)

A. Guideline Checklists

A-3 Work Control (Functions)

Independent Work Control

- Has an independent work control unit been established within the maintenance organization? <u>Y</u>

Basic Work Control Responsibilities

- Do basic control functions assigned to this unit include: centralized work reception, facility condition inspection, planning and estimating, work order preparation and approval, shop load planning, technical support for long range maintenance planning and budgeting, project management, and contract administration? <u>P</u>

Total Workload Management

- Is all work authorized for shop accomplishment processed through work control, and is work control responsible for overall work load management? <u>N</u>

Overall Effectiveness Evaluation

- Has work control been assigned responsibilities for review and evaluation of overall workload and work accomplishment, with the objectives of enhancing productivity, quality, and overall operational effectiveness and economy? <u>N</u>

Comments

Figure V.1 (cont.)

A. Guideline Checklists

A-4 Work Control (Staffing)

(The following items are appropriate primarily for medium and larger size maintenance organizations. Delete the rating and target if not appropriate.)

Work Reception Training

- Is the work reception function staffed with personnel who are familiar with facilities maintenance practices, trained to obtain complete and accurate information, and capable of providing authoritative information?

Planning Staff

- Do technicians, planner-estimators and inspectors have craft experience, and training in estimating, inspection techniques, and preparation of work orders and contracts? Are the equivalent number of planner-estimators preparing work orders staffed at a ratio of at least 1 to 40 workers?

Inspection Staff

- Are the equivalent number of facility condition inspectors staffed at a ratio of at least 1 for every 2,000,000 gross square feet to provide the capability of completing facility inspections on a two-year cycle?

Management Analysis

- Has a management analyst position been established in work control and assigned an appropriate role?

Comments

Figure V.1 (cont.)

A. Guideline Checklists

A-5 Shop Organization

Shop Functions

- Are the functions of each unit documented, and is assignment of responsibilities accompanied by the appropriate degree of authority?   Y

Lines of Authority

- Are shop policies and rules documented, distributed and practiced? Are the lines of authority clear and distinct with a minimum of vertical levels between shop head and worker?   Y

Related Crafts Relationships

- Are related craft functions grouped together to provide optimum flexibility in use of craft skills?   N

Effectiveness Evaluation

- Has the shop organization been reviewed for effectiveness during the past two years? Is shop organization centralized or decentralized? Have the specific advantages and disadvantages of each been identified and considered? Is emergency response capability adequately provided for? Are separate preventive maintenance and/or service call components established to provide more specialized and effective operations, if warranted, by organization size and workload characteristics?   N

Comments

Figure V.1 (cont.)

A. Guideline Checklists

A-6 Shop Supervision and Planning Functions

Supervisory Ratios

- Is the overall ratio of supervisors to craft workers approximately 1 to 10? For each individual craft, is the ratio between the range of 1 to 5-15?   Y

Multicraft Job Coordination

- Does the organization provide for effective coordination and supervision of multicraft jobs?   Y

Supervisory Coverage

- Is adequate supervision provided during the absence of the assigned supervisor? Are supervisors provided on every shift that subordinate personnel are required to work? If not, how is supervisory responsibility for this work handled?   N

Planning Functions

- Have shop planner and/or shop scheduling functions been established to support shop supervisors in the details of scheduling and coordinating work, procuring materials, facilitating the movement of personnel, recordkeeping, etc.?   P

Comments

Figure V.1 (cont.)

B. Effectiveness Rating Worksheet

A. Organization

			RATING	TARGET
1.	**Organization (Structure)**	7 x **1**	7	28
	Documentation not prepared or outdated	0		
	Organization Chart	①		
	Functional Statements	1		
	Job Descriptions	1		
	Active Updating Procedure	1		
2.	**Policies, Rules, Services**	7 x **4**	28	28
	Documentation not prepared or outdated	0		
	General policies, rules written	1		
	Complete policies, rules written, distributed	①		
	Complete services, written, distributed	①		
	Active updating procedure	①		
3.	**Work Control (Functions)**	9 x **2**	18	36
	Independent work control function not established	0		
	Independent work control function established	①		
	All basic work control responsibilities assigned	①		
	Process and manage total workload	1		
	Overview evaluation for effectiveness	1		
4.	**Work Control (Staffing)**	8 x **4**	32	32
	Clerical only	0		
	Work Reception, trained	①		
	Planning Staff: adequate, trained	①		
	Inspection Staff: adequate, trained	①		
	Management analysis function	①		
5.	**Shop Organization**	5 x **1**	5	20
	Documentation not prepared or outdated	0		
	Shop functions, policies, rules documented, distributed	①		
	Lines of authority clear, minimum vertical levels	1		
	Related crafts grouped together	1		
	Organization reviewed for effectiveness, past two years	1		

Figure V.2

B. Effectiveness Rating Worksheet

A. Organization

			RATING	TARGET
6.	**Shop Supervision and Planning (Functions)**	6 x **3**	18	24
	Documentation not prepared or outdated	0		
	Supervisory ratios appropriate	①		
	Coordination of multi-craft jobs	1		
	Supervisory Coverage: shifts, others	①		
	Planning functions established	①		
	Additional Comments			
	TOTAL POINTS		108	168
	PERCENTAGE		64.3%	

Figure V.2 (cont.)

B. Effectiveness Rating Worksheet

B. **Workload Identification**		RATING	TARGET
1. Facilities Inventory	5 x **4**	20	20
Records not prepared or outdated	0		
Current facility list — general data incomplete	①		
Current facility list — general data complete	①		
Current facility list — detail data complete	①		
Active Updating Procedure	①		
2. Facility Condition Inspection	9 x **3**	27	36
No structured function	0		
Scope of inspection established and personnel available	①		
Schedule established and inspections accomplished	①		
Inspections accomplished $\pm$ 10% of schedule	①		
Generate major portion of O&M-funded M&R	1		
3. Work Request Procedure	4 x **2**	8	16
Procedure not documented or outdated	0		
Procedure documented and distributed	①		
Authorization controlled	①		
Structured processing	1		
Status feedback provided to requestor	1		
4. Equipment Inventory	5 x **1**	5	20
Records not prepared or outdated	0		
Current equipment list — detail data incomplete	①		
Current equipment list — detail data complete	1		
Current equipment list — computerized	1		
Active updating procedure	1		
5. Preventive Maintenance (Equipment)	6 x **1**	6	24
No structured procedure	0		
Procedure established, includes hours, frequency, schedule	①		
Work Orders issued and personnel assigned	1		
PM accomplished $\pm$ 10% of schedule	1		
Equipment records maintained, reviewed	1		

Figure V.2 (cont.)

B. Effectiveness Rating Worksheet

B. Workload Identification		RATING	TARGET
6.	**Service Work** 6 x **2**	12	24
	Not classified separately from other types of work 0		
	Classified separately, unconstrained approval ①		
	Controlled approval, priorities identified 1		
	Structured processing procedure ①		
	Service workload analyzed, actions to reduce 1		
7.	**Routine, Recurring Work** 6 x **1**	6	24
	Not classified separately from other work 0		
	Classified separately, Work Order with general specifications ①		
	Work Order specifications quantified 1		
	Work Orders scheduled weekly in accordance with planned hours available 1		
	Work accomplished ± 10% of schedule 1		
8.	**Work Requirements Documentation** 7 x **3**	21	28
	Records not complete or readily accessible 0		
	Available but not summarized or quantifed ①		
	Quantified and summarized by requestor, priority 1		
	Summarized by status ①		
	Periodic workload review, feedback of status ①		
	Additional Comments		
	TOTAL POINTS	105	192
	PERCENTAGE	54.7%	

Figure V.2 (cont.)

B. Effectiveness Rating Worksheet

C. Workload Planning		RATING	TARGET
1. Priority Criteria	7 x <u>0</u>	0	28
No formal priority criteria established	⓪		
Priority criteria established and documented	1		
Priority criteria addresses appropriate factors	1		
Priority criteria applied consistently to all work	1		
Work performance recorded by priority and reviewed	1		
2. Work Classification	7 x <u>2</u>	14	28
Work is not classified by type of authorization	0		
Classification definitions established and documented	①		
Processing procedures are tailored to each class of work	1		
Workforce distribution targets for each class of work	1		
Work performance recorded by class of work and reviewed	①		
3. Alteration and Improvement (A/I) Work Approval	5 x <u>2</u>	10	20
A/I work is not identified separately from M&R work	0		
All A/I work processed by work control	①		
A/I fund source separated from M&R	①		
A/I work programmed with sufficient lead time	1		
Level of A/I work within ± 10% planned workforce distribution	1		
4. Work Order (WO) Preparation	10 x <u>3</u>	30	40
Written W.O. not prepared for all work	0		
W.O. issued, general description, no estimate	①		
W.O. included detail description with estimated hours and costs	1		
W.O. planned by job phase	①		
Material lists prepared	①		
5. Budget Requirements for Maintenance & Repair	7 x <u>3</u>	21	28
Based primarily on past budget amounts	0		
Based primarily on a formula approach	①		
Identifies total actual requirements	①		
Provides valid documented justification	1		
Identifies long-range requirements	①		

Figure V.2 (cont.)

B. Effectiveness Rating Worksheet

C. Workload Planning			RATING	TARGET
6.	**Backlog of Deferred Maintenance & Repair**	6 x **3**	18	24
	Not compiled or updated past 12 months	0		
	Compiled/updated past 12 months	1		
	Based on on-site condition inspection past 2 years	①		
	Funds charted and evaluated	①		
	Backlog reduction plan established	①		
7.	**Budget Execution Plan**	5 x **3**	15	20
	Execution plans not documented	0		
	Execution plan documented, month/greater	①		
	Plan identifies "classes"/"types" of work	①		
	Plan identifies specific work items	①		
	Execution controlled against plan, ± 10%	1		
8.	**Backlog of Funded Work**	5 x **1**	5	20
	Not compiled or reported periodically	0		
	Totals computed and reported monthly	①		
	Summarized by fund source, priority, shop	1		
	Reviewed periodically	1		
	Trends compiled and analyzed	1		
	Additional Comments			
	TOTAL POINTS		113	208
	PERCENTAGE			54.3%

Figure V.2 (cont.)

B. Effectiveness Rating Worksheet

D. Work Accomplishment

			RATING	TARGET
1.	**Shop Planning and Scheduling Procedures**	8 x _0_	0	32
	Formal functions not established	⓪		
	Scheduling functions established	1		
	Formal schedule procedures and planning accomplished weekly	1		
	Scheduling performance within ± 10%	1		
	Shop planning support provided	1		
2.	**Craft and Material Availability**	6 x _3_	18	24
	W.O. assigned without hour or material plan	0		
	Shop force distribution planned each week	①		
	W.O. scheduled only when craft hours are available	1		
	W.O. scheduled only when materials available	①		
	Principal materials procured and reserved	①		
3.	**Training Program**	6 x _2_	12	24
	Minimum interest indicated	0		
	Some training accomplished on unstructured basis	①		
	Training plan established and budgeted	1		
	Training plans based on needs assessment reviews	1		
	Active apprentice program	①		
4.	**Shop Spaces, Tools, Equipment**	7 x _4_	28	28
	Shop size, facilities, location inadequate	0		
	Shop size, location adequate	①		
	Shop tools, equipment adequate	①		
	Annual budget for shop replenishment	①		
	Good shop maintenance and housekeeping practices	①		
5.	**Storeroom Operation**	6 x _4_	24	24
	Limited security, accessibility, control	0		
	Secure and accessible to shops area	①		
	Control procedure and record systems established	①		
	Salvage activities and ''bench-stock'' adequately controlled	①		
	Operating information compiled for management use	①		

Figure V.2 (cont.)

B. Effectiveness Rating Worksheet

D. Work Accomplishment

			RATING	TARGET
6.	**Transportation**	5 x **2**	10	20
	Inadequate, uncontrolled	0		
	Adequate number of vehicles available	①		
	Operation and maintenance controlled	1		
	Vehicles adequately equipped	①		
	Vehicle utilization monitored and replacements programmed			
7.	**Supervisory Practices**	7 x **2**	14	28
	Insufficient time and attention to direct supervision	0		
	Percent supervisory time on direct supervision is adequate	①		
	Effective supervisory training program	1		
	Supervisory responsibilities firmly established	1		
	Supervisors actively support workers' programs; training, safety, etc.	①		
8.	**Use of Contracts**	8 x **2**	16	32
	Use of contracts is insufficient or excessive	0		
	Reasonable balance between in-house and contract	①		
	Contract specialist function established and staffed	1		
	Contractor performance monitored with a formal QA plan	1		
	Management evaluation of use of contracts	①		
	Additional Comments			
	TOTAL POINTS		122	212
	PERCENTAGE		57.5%	

Figure V.2 (cont.)

B. Effectiveness Rating Worksheet

E. Appraisal

			RATING	TARGET
1.	**Management Information System (MIS)**	8x _1_	8	32
	No structured system, inadequate/untimely reports	0		
	Basic system established with monthly reports	①		
	Reports specifically designed for each user level	1		
	System includes facility and equipment history records	1		
	Reports utilized extensively at all user levels	1		
2.	**Performance Measurement**	6 x _0_	0	24
	No effective measure of performance established	⓪		
	Estimated and actual hours/costs reported each W.O.	1		
	Performance data summarized and reported against targets	1		
	Engineered Performance Standards used as basis for W.O. estimates	1		
	Methods improvement studies conducted during past two years	1		
3.	**Productivity Measurement**	6 x _1_	6	24
	Not studied/measured during past two years	0		
	Productivity study accomplished during past two years	①		
	Productivity study included valid work sampling	1		
	Work sampling measured work categories & compared with established targets	1		
	Study results generated an improvement action plan	1		
4.	**Variance Reviews**	6 x _0_	0	24
	Not accomplished as a routine practice	⓪		
	Policy established and implemented for variance reviews	1		
	Policy assigns responsibilities and parameters	1		
	Supervisors review work-in-progress to identify variances	1		
	Are variance records maintained and reviewed	1		
5.	**Facility History Records**	6 x _2_	12	24
	Not established	0		
	Records consist primarily of completed W.O. files	①		
	Records contain adequate and current data	①		
	Data summarized and structured for review and evaluation	1		
	Analyzed quarterly	1		

Figure V.2 (cont.)

B. Effectiveness Rating Worksheet

E. Appraisal			RATING	TARGET
6.	**Equipment History Records**	6 x 0̲	**0**	24
	Not established	⓪		
	Records established for each piece of equipment	1		
	Records contain adequate and current data	1		
	Data summarized and structured for review and evaluation	1		
	Analyzed periodically as routine practice	1		
7.	**Trend Data**	7 x 1̲	**7**	28
	Not compiled	0		
	Compiled on occasional or irregular basis	①		
	Includes operational trends by performing unit	1		
	Includes longer range departmental trends	1		
	Charted routinely, major factor in overall management appraisal	1		
Additional Comments				
	TOTAL POINTS		**33**	180
	PERCENTAGE		**18.3%**	

Figure V.2 (cont.)

C. Effectiveness Rating Summary

	CURRENT RATING	TARGET
A. Organization	108	168
1. Organization (Structure)	7	28
2. Policies, Rules, Services	28	28
3. Work Control Center (Functions)	18	36
4. Work Control Center (Staffing)	32	32
5. Shop Organization	5	20
6. Shop Supervision & Planning (Functions)	18	24
B. Workload Identification	105	192
1. Facilities Inventory	20	20
2. Facility Condition Inspection	27	36
3. Work Request Procedure	8	16
4. Equipment Inventory	5	20
5. Preventive Maintenance (Equipment)	6	24
6. Service Work	12	24
7. Routine, Recurring Work	6	24
8. Work Requirements Documentation	21	28
C. Work Planning	113	208
1. Priority Criteria	0	28
2. Work Classification	14	28
3. Alterations & Improvement (A/I) Work — Approval	10	20
4. Work Order (WO) Preparation	30	40
5. Budget Requirements for M&R	21	28
6. Backlog Deferred Maintenance & Repair	18	24
7. Budget Execution Plan	15	20
8. Backlog of Funded Work	5	20
D. Work Accomplishment	122	212
1. Shop Scheduling & Planning Procedures	0	32
2. Craft and Material Availability	18	24
3. Training Program	12	24
4. Shop Spaces, Tools, Equipment	28	28
5. Storeroom Operation	24	24
6. Transportation	10	20
7. Supervisory Practices	14	28
8. Use of Contracts	16	32
E. Appraisal	33	180
1. Management Information System (MIS)	8	32
2. Performance Measurement	0	24
3. Productivity Measurement	6	24
4. Variance Reviews	0	24
5. Facility History Records	12	24
6. Equipment History Records	0	24
7. Trend Data	7	28
TOTAL POINTS	481	960
PERCENTAGE RATING	50.1%	

Worksheet V.3

The numerical rating is based on the responses to the series of questions on the Guideline Checklists. To review the rating system: The ratings of 1, 2, 3, and 4 are really 25% increments. Each increment represents another plateau or milestone of each element. A reviewer could rate each element and establish his/her own rationale for each increment. The process presented in this book and used in the case study utilizes the Guideline Checklists to establish the appropriate incremental level of accomplishment.

The increments, ratings, and descriptions are described as follows:

Increment	Rating	Description
25%	1	Poor
50%	2	Fair
75%	3	Good
100%	4	Excellent

The issue of numerical rating certainly requires some judgment and perspective. For instance, in the example shown, the component is *Organization*, the Element is *Structure*. The answers to the questions are observed as "Y, N, N, P." The reviewer recorded a score of 2 out of 4. A score of 1 would have indicated the existence of only a minimal program, but the score of 2 indicates the reviewer determined that at least an additional level of development was in place. This is evidenced by the "P" (partial) answer to one question.

To clear up the issue of responses "Y," "N," or "P," and scores of 1-4, it may be helpful to look at a table of typical responses and scores.

Typical Scores

Observed	Likely Score
N, N, N, N, N	0
Y, Y, Y, Y, Y	4
Y, N, N, N, N	1
Y, Y, P, N, N	2 or 3
P, P, P, P, P	2 or 3
Y, Y, Y, N, N	3

This table is by no means all the possible combinations of Y's, N's, or P's, but the possible scores are only 1, 2, 3, or 4. The above table shows that there is some latitude in possible ratings, but this is somewhat offset by having a single reviewer with one point of view assign the ratings. In this way, it is hoped that each component or element will receive equal treatment.

A final observation on responses and scores: A series of responses written as "N," "N," "N," "Y" is probably an error. The questions are in, more or less, incremental order. So a series of "no" answers with a final "yes" should be rechecked. In that case, some of the previous "no" answers should probably be "Ps," or the final "Y" should be rewritten as a "P."

A review of the checklists and Effectiveness Rating Summary identified a number of areas with low observed ratings and obvious areas for potential improvements.

Action Plan

Once the last reviewer completed the checklists and summary sheets, the last remaining issue was the development of an action plan to implement the changes and improvements. To develop an action plan, the reviewer revisited the individual Guideline Checklists. The checklists are written in such a way that the questions themselves indicate the solution.

To illustrate the process, the following component, "Organization," will be discussed as follows: Figure V.4 is the Effectiveness Rating Worksheet for the organization. It clearly shows a rating of 108 out of 168.

Figure V.5 shows the component, "Organization," along with the six elements that it is comprised of. The rating that each element received is shown (shaded), as compared to the total possible rating. Each element is also shown from left to right, in terms of priority for action. In other words, the first element to address in identifying action items is the structure of the organization.

The elements to consider in priority order are:

1. Structure
2. Shop Organization
3. Work Control Center (Functions)
4. Shop Supervision and Planning

The main question is: what actions are necessary to improve the elements in the component, "Organization?" The answer lies in the checklist questions themselves and in the associated analysis of each question.

Figure V.1 is the first Guideline Checklist. The listed responses are "yes," "no," "no," "no," "no," and "p" (partial).

The first "no" response is to the question concerning functional statements. The lack of functional statements is a fundamental issue in an organization assessment. Therefore, the "no" response is converted into a required action: Prepare functional statements.

By noting all Guideline Checklist items with a "no" or "partial" response, the reviewer can immediately develop a list of required actions. Figure V.6 takes all "n" or "p" responses for the "Organization" components and utilizes them to develop a list of actions (an Action Plan).

Assignment of Responsibility

The next issues to be resolved are who is going to implement (or be responsible for) these actions, and what level of effort (in labor hours or dollars) will be required.

Again, focusing for the moment on "Organization," Figure V.6, there are four items to address.

1. Structure
2. Shop Organization
3. Work Control Center (Functions)
4. Shop Supervision and Planning

An action would be developed first for 1. Structure. The next would be Shop Organization, and so forth.

To illustrate, Shop Organization is explained as follows: Shop Organization has five required actions (see Figure V.6) that must be addressed. Our team received each of those actions and, with in-house management, made general assignments of who will take the "lead" role in their implementation. Figure V.7 shows the result of that assignment.

B. Effectiveness Rating Worksheet

A. Organization

		RATING	TARGET
6. **Shop Supervision and Planning (Functions)**	6 x **3**	18	24
Documentation not prepared or outdated	0		
Supervisory ratios appropriate	①		
Coordination of multi-craft jobs	1		
Supervisory Coverage: shifts, others	①		
Planning functions established	①		
Additional Comments			
TOTAL POINTS		108	168
PERCENTAGE			64.3%

Figure V.4

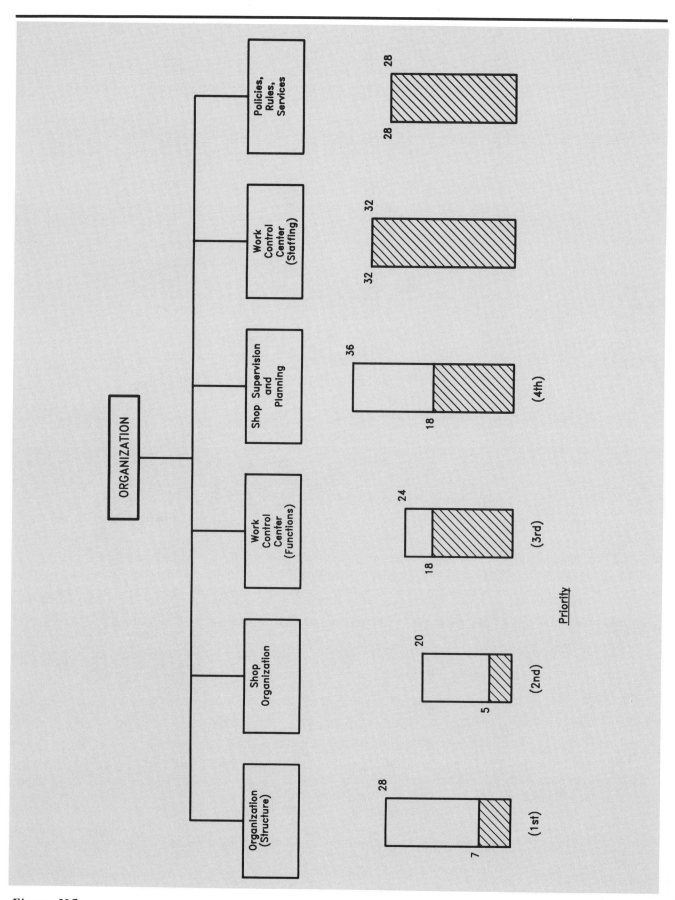

Figure V.5

108

Component Action
Items For
ORGANIZATION

1. **Structure**

   a. Prepare functional statements

   b. Prepare job descriptions

   c. Develop, schedule, perform annual reviews

   d. Update organization responsibilities

   e. Incorporate required changes in organization chart

2. **Shop organization**

   a. Clarify lines of authority

   b. Regroup shop crafts

   c. Review shop effectiveness (bi-annually)

   d. Document emergency response capability

   e. Establish separate PM and service call shops

3. **Work control center (functions)**

   a. Include key functions (see checklist)

   b. Authorize all work to be performed by shops

   c. Develop productivity guidelines for WCC

4. **Shop supervision and planning**

   a. Develop and initiate adequate "off-hours" supervision

   b. Develop and initiate absentee supervision

   c. Initiate job planning fundamentals (see checklist)

Figure V.6

Responsibility Matrix

Action	Fac. Mgmt. Dept.	Shop Super.	Personnel Dept.	Outside Consultant
Shop Organization				
A. Clarify lines			3–6 Mo.	
B. Regroup crafts		6–12 Mo.		
C. Rv. effectiveness				12–24 Mo.
D. Doc. capability	1–3 Mo.*			
E. Est. shops	3–6 Mo.			

(Number of months refers to the total elapsed time that our review determined was sufficient to incorporate those actions.)

Figure V.7

Carrying the process a step further, the action and responsibility for Shop Organization can be estimated as follows:

Estimated Labor Hours to Complete:

Milestone	A	B	C	D	E
Prepare Draft	80	16	500	120	160
Circulate for comments	24	8	300	80	80
Incorporate comments	16	4	120	60	40
Prepare final	8	4	80	40	40
Total	128	32	1,000	300	320

The estimated labor hours should be based on an established level of detail for each action item. The numbers used in this case study were based on the specific needs of the local maintenance department.

A GANTT-type chart is then developed to spread each element across a calendar format to track sequence, progress, and start/finish times. Applying the actions, responsibilities, and estimates the following chart in Figure V.8 developed.

Actions required to improve the Organizational component, Structure, comprised approximately 1,700 labor hours over the next 24 months. Estimating levels of effort enables the manager to budget, or seek additional funds to implement the required actions.

Summary and Conclusions

The case study describes the management audit for a medium-sized university. The specific numbers and resulting action plans are valid only for the case study site. The process described in Chapters 1 through 4 allows the reader to perform a complete management audit on any facility intensive organization such as:

- large office buildings
- multiple building office parks
- banks with multiple branches
- colleges and universities
- hotel/motel chains
- military installations
- manufacturing/shipping installations
- city facilities
- state governments

There are many advantages of conducting a management audit of your site using the techniques and forms provided in this book, including:

- The process provides a tremendous opportunity to analyze and/or establish the goals of the maintenance organization.
- The audit allows you to evaluate the organization's succession accomplishing its goals, and whether these goals are met in the most effective manner. It answers the question: are you getting the most for your maintenance dollar?
- The process provides you with a detailed analysis of facilities maintenance by looking at the five basic components, namely:
  — organization
  — workload identification
  — work planning
  — work accomplishment
  — appraisal

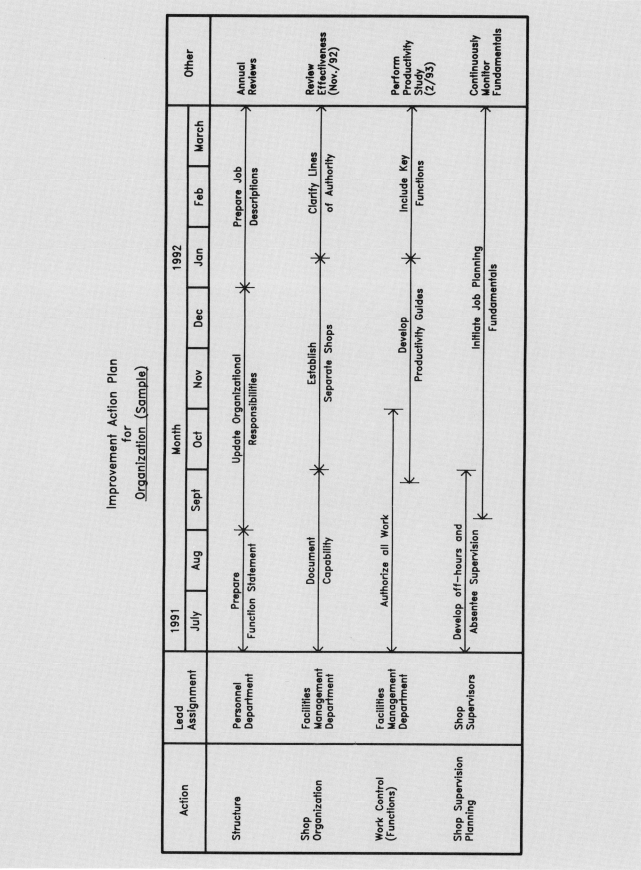

Improvement Action Plan
for
Organization (Sample)

Action	Lead Assignment	1991		Month				1992			Other
		July	Aug	Sept	Oct	Nov	Dec	Jan	Feb	March	
Structure	Personnel Department	Prepare Function Statement			Update Organizational Responsibilities				Prepare Job Descriptions		Annual Reviews
Shop Organization	Facilities Management Department	Document Capability				Establish Separate Shops			Clarify Lines of Authority		Review Effectiveness (Nov./92)
Work Control (Functions)	Facilities Management Department	Authorize all Work					Develop Productivity Guides		Include Key Functions		Perform Productivity Study (2/93)
Shop Supervision Planning	Shop Supervisors	Develop off-hours and Absentee Supervision					Initiate Job Planning Fundamentals				Continuously Monitor Fundamentals

Figure V.8

111

- The detailed perspective of the management system provides a method of relative ratios for an accurate assessment of productivity and other criteria.
- Analysis of the Guideline checklist results yields a specific set of action items and prioritizes the actions required.
- The prioritized items form the outline for a schedule and an estimate (labor hours and cost) to accomplish the required actions.

This workbook is based on the management precept that there is always room for improvement. Typically, improvement can be difficult to accomplish or evaluate due to the complexity of maintenance management. The audit program presented in this book provides a uniform evaluation of Maintenance Effectiveness and Improvement, which can simplify the evaluation process.

As noted in the Foreword, the process outlined in this book can take the form of a preliminary audit or a full-fledged, comprehensive, multi-layered management audit. Used as a preliminary audit, this process can set the stage for a more orderly, prioritized large scale review of maintenance resources.

Index

A

A/I work *See* alteration and
    improvement work.
accountability, 28
action items for organization, 107
action plan, 9, 28, 30, 105
    improvement, 27, 29
active updating procedure, 37
advantages of the management
    audit, 110, 112
alteration and improvement work, 53
    approval, 78
Applied Management Engineering, 15
appraisal, 26
apprentice program, 61
assignment of responsibility, 106, 109
audit
    forms, 33-84
    goals, 19
    process, assessing the, 28, 30
    performing the, 5
    phasing, 3
    team, 4-5
authority, 41

B

backlog, 56, 79
    of funded work, 58, 79
bench stock controls, 63
budget
    documentation, 55
    execution, 57
    execution plan, 79
    requirements for maintenance and
        repair, 55, 78
budgetary methods, 55

C

case study, 85-112
checklists, guideline, 37-73
consultants, 19
contracts, use of, 66, 81

coordinator, role of, 5
cost reporting, 55
CPM path, 27
craft
    availability, 60, 80
    relationships, 41

D

Department of Defense, 10, 14
documentation, work requirements, 50

E

effectiveness of the audit, 9-10
effectiveness rating, 9
    compiling the, 22-26
Effectiveness Rating Summary, 26, 84,
    104
    overview of, 20
Effectiveness Rating Worksheets, 24,
    25, 74-83
    filled out, 94-103
efficiency, 9
elements of the audit, 11-12
engineered performance standards, 68
equipment, 62, 80
    history records, 72, 83
    inventory, 46, 76

F

facilities inventory, 28, 43, 76
facility condition inspection, 44, 76
facility history records, 71, 82
FCI *See* facility condition inspection.
follow-up of results, 6
forms, 33-84
    use of, 35-36
function statements, 37
funded work backlog, 58, 79

G

GANTT chart, 27, 110
goals of audit, 19

Guideline Checklists, 37-73
    filled out, 88-93

I

Improvement Action Plan, 27-29
    for organization (sample), 111
improvement, identifying
    opportunities for, 27
inspection, 44
introduction to the maintenance
    management audit process, 7-15
inventory, 43
    control, 11
    equipment, 76

J

job descriptions, 37
job phasing, 54

M

maintenance management audit,
    purpose of, 3
Management Information Systems, 11,
    67, 82
management action, 5
management analysis, 40
management audit
    definition of, vii
    process, 4
management effectiveness analysis, 14
manufacturing productivity, 9
material
    availability, 60
    requirement, 54
MIS *See* Management Information
    System.

O

operations, efficiency of, 9
organization, 11-12, 24, 26
    chart, 37

P

performance measurement, 68
performance, 9
phase descriptions, 4
policies, 38
    rules, services, 24
preliminary program review, 9, 21
preliminary suggestions, 3
preventive maintenance
    (equipment), 47, 76
prioritization, 10, 50
priority criteria, 51, 78
processing procedures, 53
productivity, 9, 14
    definition of, 10
    manufacturing, 9
    measurement, 69, 82
program review, preliminary, 21
purchasing, 11
purpose of the audit, 9

Q

quality of work, 10

R

rating criteria, 35
ratings, 14
recurring work, 49
report, preparing the, 5
responsibility matrix, 109
results, evaluating, 28
results questionnaire, 31
review
    procedures, 9
    process, 13-16
routine work, 49
routine, recurring work, 77
rules, 38

S

schedule, audit, 4
scheduling, 59
services, 38
service work, 48, 77
shop
    functions, 41
    organization, 24
    planning and scheduling
      procedures, 42, 59, 80
    spaces, 62, 80
staff planning, 40
standing work order performance
    reporting, 49
steering committee, vii, 28
storeroom operation, 63, 80
summary, effectiveness rating, 84
supervision and planning, 25, 42
supervisory
    practices and training, 65, 81
    ratios, 42

T

team, forming the audit, 4
tools, 62, 80
training, 61
    program, 80
    work reception, 40
transportation, 64, 81
trend data, 73, 83

V

variance reviews, 70, 82

W

work
    accomplishment, 11-12, 26, 80
    classification, 52, 78
    control, 24
    control functions, 39
    control staffing, 40
    planning, 11-12, 26
    quality, 10
    request procedure, 45, 76
    requirements documentation, 50,
      77
    work force distribution, 53
workload
    analysis, 48
    identification, 11-12, 26, 28, 76

management,   39
planning,   78
work order,   47
preparation,   54, 78
scheduling,   49
specification,   49
records,   71
worksheets, effectiveness
rating,   74-83

Maintenance Audit Forms
On Diskette

Complete the audit on your PC!

The maintenance audit forms presented in this book can be generated on your computer using our Maintenance Audit Forms Diskette, which will enable you to:

- Modify any form to meet your facility's specific conditions.

- Personalize forms with company or departmental identification.

- Print the forms in the most convenient format.

- Save space by keeping audits on disk!

Available in 5¼″ or 3½″ diskettes in:

- Wordperfect

- Multimate

- Microsoft Word

TO ORDER, call 1-800-448-8182 or send in the order blank below.

Only $19.95